Ellen's mum sighed. Then she looked at Ellen. "Actually, your spots do look quite a bit better," she said. "That one on your nose has disappeared. And look!" she added, picking something out of the basin. "Here's your left slipper."

Ellen said nothing, but she smiled as she put the slipper on.

She knew that it wasn't really her slipper. It belonged to Princess Mirror-Belle.

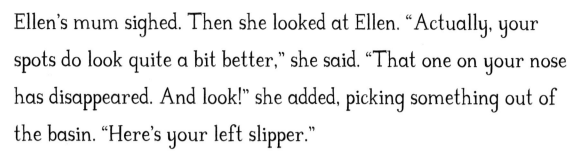

"... 98, 99, 100!" Ellen ripped the paper off her face and opened her eyes. "Where are you, Mirror-Belle?" she asked.

She looked around the empty room and saw that the door handle was turning.

But it wasn't Mirror-Belle. Instead, Ellen's mum came into the room.

"Ellen, what *have* you been doing?" she said, as she looked at the watery foamy room and all the empty tubes and bottles.

"It wasn't me, it was Princess Mirror-Belle," said Ellen. "She came out of the mirror. She was trying to cure my dragon pox ... I mean, chicken pox."

"Oh, and I suppose she's gone back into the mirror now?" said Ellen's mum.

Ellen looked at the mirror over the basin. It was covered in toothpasty bubbles. "Yes, I think she has," she said.

"I thought I told you to
stop asking questions," said Mirror-Belle.
"Now, it's time to get dry and put our pyjamas back on."
"But we're still all spotty," said Ellen as she put on her slipper.
"The cure hasn't worked."
"Ah, that's because we haven't done part two yet," said Mirror-Belle.
"What's part two?" asked Ellen.
"This!" Mirror-Belle picked up a roll of loo paper and started
to wind it round and round Ellen, who laughed.
"What about you?" she asked.
"We'll do me later," said Mirror-Belle, carrying on
winding. Before long Ellen's whole body was covered
in loo paper and Mirror-Belle had started on her face.
Then, "Close your eyes and count to a hundred!"
she said. So Ellen did.

"I'll tell you later," said Mirror-Belle, and she splashed some frothy creamy foamy toothpasty bath water at Ellen. Ellen giggled and splashed some back. This was beginning to be fun.

But then she noticed that the bathroom floor was getting really wet from all the splashing. "Oh dear, my mum will be a bit cross," she said.

"Really? How peculiar. My mother the Queen is cross if I *don't* splash the floor. In fact she likes me to splash it so much that the whole bathroom is like a paddling pool. Then she paddles about in it to wash her feet, and so do all the palace maids."

"Doesn't the water drip down onto the floor below?" asked Ellen.

Mirror-Belle didn't reply. Instead, she poured a bottle of shampoo into the bath.

"How will we wash our hair now?" asked Ellen.

"I wouldn't bother washing it," said Mirror-Belle. "When my hair gets dirty I just say a magic spell and wish for some different hair. My hair doesn't always look like yours, you know. Last week I had golden curls and the week before I had . . . er, red ringlets."

"I'd love to do that," said Ellen. "What is the magic spell?"

"I do wish you wouldn't ask so many questions," said Mirror-Belle. "Let's get on with the cure. How about this?" And she squirted in some white foam from a spray can.

"Stop!" cried Ellen. "That's my dad's shaving cream."

"Well, I think he should stop shaving, like my father the King," said Mirror-Belle.

"Does your father have a beard then?" asked Ellen.

"Of course he does. It's so long it reaches the ground. He needs two servants to walk ahead of him to carry it. And sometimes birds make their nests in it."

Ellen laughed. "And do the birds fly in and out feeding worms to their babies?" she asked.

"Hmm, we need some more ingredients," said Mirror-Belle when they were both in the bath.

"Let's try this." Before Ellen could stop her, she had squirted a whole tube of toothpaste into the water.

"Hey, now we won't be able to clean our teeth," Ellen protested.

"But can't you get the fairies to clean your teeth?" asked Mirror-Belle.

"No – I don't know any fairies. And what would they use instead of toothpaste?"

"Well, our fairies collect dewdrops from rose petals and use that," said Mirror-Belle.

"How does it stick on the toothbrushes?" asked Ellen.

"Now then," said Mirror-Belle.
"On with the cure! This stuff looks good."
She grabbed a bottle of bubble bath
and squirted it into the water.
Then, "How odd!" she exclaimed, as
hundreds of bubbles appeared.

"Don't you have bubble bath
back home?" asked Ellen.

"Certainly not," said Mirror-Belle.
"But we do have bubble fish. They're
much better. They swim about in
the bath and blow thousands of bubbles."

"But isn't the bath water a bit hot
for the fish?" asked Ellen.

"Never mind that," said Mirror-Belle.
"Let's get in."

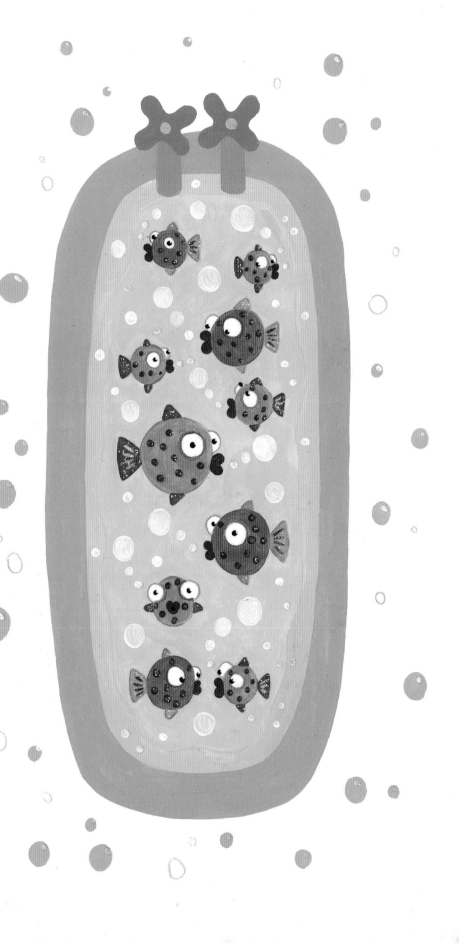

"Never mind that," said Mirror-Belle. "We need to get started on the cure for dragon pox." And she put the plug in the bath and turned on the taps.

"But I haven't got dragon pox," said Ellen.

"Well, I have," Mirror-Belle said firmly. "You see, a dragon captured me last week and carried me off to his mountain lair. Luckily a knight came and rescued me, but when I got home I came out in these terrible spots."

"Did the knight want to marry you?" asked Ellen. But Mirror-Belle seemed not to hear her.

"Don't be silly," said the mirror girl, and the next second she had jumped out of the mirror and was in the bathroom with Ellen. "I'm Princess Mirror-Belle. You really ought to curtsey, but as you're my friend I'll let you off."

"Are you really a princess?" asked Ellen. "But you look just like me. You've got the same pyjamas. You've even lost one of your slippers like me."

"Oh no I haven't," said Mirror-Belle. She paused for a second and then continued: "My slipper was stolen by a goblin. They're always stealing slippers. They like to sleep in them."

Ellen laughed. "Do they have little sheets and pillows?" she asked.

Then she jumped, when a voice from the mirror said, "Don't scratch! You might turn into a toad!"

Could this really be happening? Could Ellen's reflection really be talking to her? Before Ellen could reply, the mirror girl went on: "You've got really bad dragon pox."

"No I haven't," said Ellen. "I've got *chicken* pox. And so have you. You're my reflection."

Ellen had chicken pox. She was covered in spots.

"You mustn't scratch them!" said Mum.

Ellen put on her right slipper (she had lost the left one) and went to look at her spots in the bathroom mirror. The spot on her nose was so itchy! Surely a tiny little scratch wouldn't do any harm? Ellen lifted a finger to her nose . . .

Written by   Illustrated by

JULIA DONALDSON ★ LYDIA MONKS

Princess Mirror-Belle
and the Dragon Pox

MACMILLAN CHILDREN'S BOOKS

For Lauren

First published 2014 by Macmillan Children's Books
This edition published 2015 by Macmillan Children's Books
an imprint of Pan Macmillan, a division of
Macmillan Publishers Limited
20 New Wharf Road, London N1 9RR
Associated companies throughout the world
www.panmacmillan.com

ISBN: 978-1-4472-4020-4

Text copyright © Julia Donaldson 2014
Illustrations copyright © Lydia Monks 2014
Moral rights asserted.

1 3 5 7 9 8 6 4 2

A CIP catalogue record for this book is available from the British Library.

Printed in China

contents

INTRODUCTION 4

CHAPTER ONE: ENJOY 5

CHAPTER TWO: GIVE 94

CHAPTER THREE: USE 141

CHAPTER FOUR: HOLD 221

TEMPLATES 288

INDEX 312

Introduction

Celebrate 100 of the prettiest little projects ever! For three fabulous years, Lark editors curated and published eight books in the Pretty Little series, showcasing the work of some of the most talented craft designers in the world. It's our distinct honor to present this best-of-the-best compilation to you. And what makes these the best-of-the-best? Because we loved them, that's why.

The first book, *Pretty Little Pincushions*, was such a runaway success that we added titles as quickly as we could; patchwork and potholders followed soon, jumping on those hot trends. We filled books with purses and pouches, as well as cozies and presents. The final books in the series, featuring mini-quilts and pillows, contained projects that were just as cute and quirky and fun as the previous books. They were each a joy to work on.

The wonderful thing about all of these delightful creations is that none of these projects require advanced sewing skills—if you own a sewing machine, you're probably familiar with most, if not all, of the techniques required to create any of these adorable things. Consult your favorite sewing book or do a quick Internet search if you need help with a specific topic, but trust us—most of these little treasures are as fun and easy to make as they are lovely to behold.

We've organized our favorites into loose categories: Enjoy, Use, Hold, and Give. The projects in the Enjoy chapter are eye-candy, like decorative quilts and pillows; the Use chapter is full of handy things like potholders and pincushions; discover lots of things that hug everything from your yoga mat to your nighttime reading in the Hold section; and delight in the perfect present from the Give chapter. So what are you waiting for? Pick one of our very best—and prettiest—projects and get started.

enjoy

sitting pretty cushion 6

sweet dreams 9

one tree hill 12

hearts on fire 14

feeling needled 18

too cool cuff 20

autumn breeze 24

book nook 27

in bloom 30

yard tale 32

soft spheres 36

hop in your step 38

birdie mobile 40

obi belt 44

refab modern 47

flowing scarf 52

square deal 54

center of attention 57

blue pools 59

the elusive batiki bird 62

quick change 66

that's amore 70

airborne appliqué 73

bonbon brooch 76

cuddle drops 79

bright teeth 82

spinning in orbit 85

spiffy potholders 88

child's play 91

sitting *pretty* cushion

Move over, curds and whey—this little cushion turns Miss Muffet into Miss Magnifique. With sweet ribbon detailing, rickrack, and beads, you'll be sitting pretty in no time.

DESIGNER

JOAN K. MORRIS

WHAT YOU NEED

Basic sewing tools

15-inch-round (38.1 cm) pillow form with flat sides

6 assorted print cotton fabrics, ¼ yard (21.6 cm) each

Paper-backed fusible web

6 assorted ribbons, rickrack, and trim

Invisible thread

Matching thread

10 to 12 glass beads or buttons

½ yard (45.7 cm) striped upholstery fabric

3 yards (2.7 m) of cord for piping

½ yard (45.7 cm) more of one of the print cotton fabrics for the piping

Zipper foot

Spray adhesive

1 yard (.91 cm) quilt batting

1 yard (.91 m) light colored embroidery floss

Embroidery needle (long with large eye)

2 covered buttons, 1¼ inch (3.2 cm)

SEAM ALLOWANCE

½ inch (1.3 cm)

WHAT YOU DO

1 Trace the pillow form onto the scrap paper. Add ½ inch (1.3 cm) all the way around the edge, and cut out. Fold the circle in half, and then fold the half in thirds to get the size of the six triangles minus the seam allowance. Trace the shape, and add ½ inch (1.3 cm) to the sides. Cut this out.

2 With this pattern, cut out a triangle from each of the six print cotton fabrics. Machine stitch three triangles side by side with a ½-inch (1.3 cm) seam allowance. Pin the seams before sewing if needed. Press the seams flat, then machine stitch the other three triangles together, and press flat. Pin the two pieces together, and machine stitch to create the circle. Press the seam open.

3 Cut out 6-inch (15.2 cm) squares of each of the six fabrics, and cut six 6-inch (15.2 cm) squares of the fusible web. Following the manufacturer's instructions, adhere it to the back of each of the pieces of fabric. On the paper backing, draw the flowers, circles, and leaves you want to place on the pillow. Cut the flowers out.

4 Position the flowers on the cushion top, and add the ribbons as stems until you get a design you like. Remove the flowers, leaving the ribbon in place, and pin in position. With invisible thread in the top of the machine and matching thread in the bobbin, machine zigzag the ribbon in place.

5 Following the manufacturer's instructions, remove the paper backing, and iron the flowers and leaves in position. On top of the flowers, iron on the centers.

Machine zigzag the flowers and leaves in position with the invisible thread on top and regular thread in the bobbin. Place the 10 to 12 glass beads and buttons in position, and hand stitch them with needle and thread.

6 From the striped fabric, cut a circle the same size as the

top cushion. Cut out a strip 3 inches (7.6 cm) wide from the striped fabric with a length that equals the total measurement around the pillow plus 1/2 inch (1.3 cm).

7 Measure around the pillow, and add 2 inches (5.1 cm) to the measurement. This will be the length of each of the two pieces of piping. Cut the fabric on the diagonal, and make it 2 inches wide by the length measured. You'll need to piece fabric together to make it long enough. When piecing bias, place the ends of the fabric at 90° angles, stitch from corner to corner, and cut off the excess corner.

8 To make the piping, place the cord in the center of the fabric you cut in step 7 and, with the zipper foot, stitch as close as you can to the cord.

9 With the zipper foot still on, machine baste the piping in place on the top and bottom pieces. Do this by placing the piping around the edge, with the raw edge of the piping lining up with the raw edge of the circle. Start stitching 1 inch (2.5 cm) from the edge of the piping. Where the two ends meet, cut the piping cord to

the exact length. Put the two ends right sides together, and stitch across at the proper length. Push the cord back in place, and finish stitching the piping.

10 Cut pieces of the quilt batting to cover the pillow form, and glue in place with the spray adhesive. Place the cushion top upside down on the pillow form. Wrap the 3-inch (7.6 cm) strip of striped fabric around the form, wrong side out. Pin the edges of the top and the side strip together and stitch in a 1/2-inch (1.3 cm) seam allowance, using a zipper foot. Stitch the ends of the 3-inch (7.6 cm) strip together.

11 Stitch the bottom piece to the other side of the 3-inch (7.6 cm) strip; leave open about a third so the pillow will fit inside. Clip curves. Turn right side out.

12 Stuff the pillow inside. Pin the opening closed, and then hand stitch the opening closed.

13 Thread the embroidery floss onto the needle, and double the thread. From the top, run the needle through the center of the pillow to the back, leaving half the embroidery floss on top. Run the needle back up to the front. Pull both ends of the embroidery floss tight, tie a knot, and pull it tightly.

14 Following the manufacturer's instructions, cover the two buttons with the striped fabric. With regular thread and needle, stitch one of the covered buttons on each side.

PIECE IT TOGETHER

If you don't have a piece of fabric that can make a strip in the length you need in step 6, piece one together. If you do, add a 1/2-inch (1.3 cm) seam allowance between the pieces.

sweetdreams

$\mathcal{T}$his one's a softy—it features nostalgic fabric, a sweet and simple design, and a soothing scent, too.

DESIGNER

TONI WEBER

WHAT YOU NEED

Basic sewing tools

Ruler

Fabric chalk

Sewing machine (optional)

Iron

Embroidery floss, coordinating color

Button

WHAT YOU DO

1 Using a ruler and fabric chalk, draw an 8 x 5½-inch rectangle directly onto your fabric. Double the fabric and cut two rectangles.

2 Pin the rectangles with wrong sides together, and sew a ¼-inch seam on all sides, leaving one narrow edge opening for turning. Clip the corners and turn the rectangle right-side out.

3 Tuck the open edges under, matching the rest of the seam, and press. Stuff the pincushion with polyester fiberfill. Be sure to pack the corners, but don't overstuff. Hand stitch the opening closed.

4 Thread a needle with a long strand of embroidery floss. Starting in the center of the bottom, poke the needle up through the center top and pull the floss through, leaving a 2-inch tail below. Hold the tail down, and wrap the floss around one side of the pillow. Bring the needle back to the bottom and push up though the center again. Give the floss a slight tug and wrap the next side (figure 1). Repeat for all sides to tuft the cushion.

5 With the needle at the center top, pass it through the button and back through the pincushion. Repeat again. Then knot the loose ends on the bottom of the pincushion and trim the excess. Tie the loose ends together in a knot and clip off the excess.

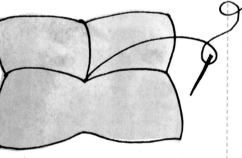

Figure 1

STAB AND SNIFF

As you're stuffing this cushion, add dried lavender or chamomile. Just make sure you include a top and bottom layer of polyester fiberfill. (And, if you've already stuck pins in, this isn't the place to lay your head down.)

onetreehill

A few scraps of fabric and some embroidery floss combine to form this charming scene of blue sky, white cloud, green tree and hill, and scampering brown squirrel. Take this general technique and run with it to decorate your walls with your own peaceful vistas.

WHAT YOU NEED

Basic sewing tools

Colored, patterned fabrics in aqua blue, lime green, and white

Thread in complementary colors

Embroidery floss in dark and light brown, dark and light green, light blue, dark and light coral

Embroidery needle

Embroidery hoop

8 x 8-inch (20.3 x 20.3 cm) wood canvas frame

Staple gun

SEAM ALLOWANCE

¼ inch (0.6 cm)

DESIGNER

AIMEE RAY

WHAT YOU DO

1 Cut different sizes of squares and rectangles from the aqua fabrics. Piece them together at random to make a square at least 10 x 10 inches (25.4 x 25.4 cm).

2 Using the project photo as a guide, cut squares and rectangles from the green fabrics, and sew them together in rows, enough to cover the hill section of the picture. Fold over ¼ inch (0.6 cm) of the edge of the green piece into a curve to make the hill shape and press. Use the appliqué stitch to sew the hill in place at the corner of the aqua square.

3 Cut a few more squares of green fabric, and sew them together. Cut the oval tree shape from this piece. Then cut two oval cloud shapes from the white fabric. Press the edges ¼ inch (0.6 cm) in, and stitch them in place on the aqua background.

4 Embroider the tree trunk, hill and cloud lines, flowers, and squirrel as shown in the photo.

5 Center the art piece over the frame. Fold the sides over the back, and staple them in place with a staple in both the top and bottom and one in each side. Continue pulling the fabric tightly and stapling it down along each side of the frame.

ARTISTIC LICENSE

If you decide to design your own fabric masterpiece, remember that you're creating a 10-inch-square (25.4 cm) overall piece with an 8-inch (20.3 cm) square visible from the front.

hearts on fire

DESIGNER

CINDY COOKSEY

$\mathcal{E}$ach of the hearts in this warm-toned quilt may differ in texture, color, and embellishment, but together they beat as one to make a beautiful design.

WHAT YOU NEED

Basic sewing tools

Background fabric, 18 x 16 inches (45.7 x 40.6 cm)

Low-loft batting, 18 x 16 inches (45.7 x 40.6 cm)

Cotton backing fabric, 18 x 16 inches (45.7 x 40.6 cm)

Contrasting thread for basting

16 scrap pieces of mostly red fabric for hearts, each at least 3 x 4 inches (7.6 x 10.2 cm)

Thin fusible web

Parchment paper or release paper to use with fabric fuse

Machine-quilting thread to match hearts

Perle cotton embroidery thread in a variety of weights in red, black, burgundy, and variegated

Metallic embroidery thread in silver and gold

Dark red metallic or similar fabric for binding, ¼ yard (22.9 cm)

Embellishments such as a red fabric-covered button, red beads (seed, bugle, and flat round), heart-shaped and other buttons or beads in red, metallic, or black

SEAM ALLOWANCE

None

FINISHED SIZE

14½ x 17 inches (36.8 x 43.2 cm)

WHAT YOU DO

1 Make a sandwich of the background fabric, batting, and cotton backing fabric. Pin together.

2 Baste around the outer edge. Then use a ruler and pins to locate a vertical line down the middle, and baste along the line. Use the same method to locate a horizontal line in the exact middle, and baste along that line. The basting lines will keep the silk background fabric from shifting around, and they will also help with placing the hearts.

3 Back most of the sixteen 3 x 4-inch (7.6 x 10.2 cm) fabric scraps with fusible web according to the manufacturer's instructions. Use release paper or parchment

SWEET HEARTS ARE MADE OF THIS

For the hearts, you can use a variety of silks, chiffon, velvet, lace, and sheers, with some solid and some printed or machine embroidered. Consider unexpected materials such as window screen and plastic "fishnet" material from a produce bag as well.

paper to protect surfaces from any melted fusible web. Some materials such as lace, window screen, and plastic fishnet will not be appropriate for fusing.

4 Trace a heart shape onto paper and cut out.

5 Pin the paper heart shape onto each fabric scrap and carefully cut out fabric hearts. There is no seam allowance.

6 Arrange the hearts on the prepared background fabric sandwich. Use the center horizontal and vertical lines to guide in placement: Place the tops of four hearts right along the horizontal line, with the bottom tips of the next row up also just touching the horizontal line. Center the hearts horizontally and place them about ½ inch (1.3 cm) apart vertically.

7 When you are happy with the arrangement, carefully iron down the hearts with fusible web on them, taking great care to keep the iron away from any window screen, plastic fishnet, or other materials that may be damaged by the heat. Pin the hearts without fusible web in place.

8 Some of the fused hearts can now be stitched down with free-motion machine quilting. Use thread that best goes with each heart—red in most cases. Stitch close to the edges, and stitch along the fabric design if desired. Leave some heart centers unquilted for later embellishment.

9 Use a hand blanket stitch around the edges of two or three of the fused hearts. Use contrasting embroidery thread such as black and metallic.

10 Use other hand embroidery to stitch down the edges of the unfused hearts, such as crisscross Xs and straight lines pointing inward.

11 Couch burgundy eyelash yarn around one heart (optional).

12 Using red perle cotton embroidery thread (red-to-burgundy hand-dyed if you can find it), hand embroider the

background fabric with random scattered stitches, about ³/₈ inch (9.5 mm) long. Make the stitches go in all directions. Continue the stitches to make a 1½-inch (3.8 cm) border on the background fabric, taking care not to extend stitches beyond this border.

13 Remove the basting thread, then trim the quilt with a rotary cutter, leaving a 1½-inch (3.8 cm) border around the hearts. This will make your quilt about 14½ inches (36.8 cm) wide and 17 inches (43.2 cm) tall.

14 Apply binding using your preferred method.

15 Embellish the centers of several hearts, but leave a few interesting ones unembellished to stand on their own. Suggestions for embellishing: Stitch a large button or charm in each upper center of several hearts. Use seed beads scattered randomly on one heart, and in snake patterns on another. Use bugle beads, round flat beads, random-sized smaller red buttons, and other distinctive-looking beads, either scattered randomly or following the design on the fabric.

16 Use extra backing fabric to create a sleeve for hanging.

feelingneedled

$\mathcal{N}$ot ready to forgive and forget? Maybe this guy is who you're looking for...

DESIGNER

JOAN K. MORRIS

WHAT YOU NEED

Basic sewing tools

Felt, gray and white

Sewing machine (optional)

Black thread

Embroidery floss, black and red

WHAT YOU DO

1 Create patterns from the templates (page 288). Cut two top pieces from white felt and two bottom pieces from gray felt.

2 Machine stitch each white top to a bottom gray across the waist. With wrong sides together, machine stitch around the figure with a ⅛-inch exposed seam allowance. Start and end at the head, leaving the top open for stuffing.

3 Stuff the figure tightly with polyester fiberfill, starting at the feet and working toward the head. Machine stitch the opening closed.

4 With black embroidery floss, whipstitch hair on the head. Stitch an X for the eyes and a line for the mouth. Use a short running stitch for the hands, center circle, and shoe laces. Sew red embroidery floss in a satin stitch for the heart.

Woman Variation

Using the woman pattern, follow the same instructions as for the man. Change the lips to red, add more hair, and sew french knots for the necklace and bracelet. Use a buttonhole stitch for the dress hem, and a detached chain stitch for the flower.

too cool cuff

A cuff this cool is twice as nice
with reversible snaps that let you show
off your best side. Any way you flip it,
this cuff's the stuff.

DESIGNER

LAUREN HUNT

WHAT YOU NEED

Basic sewing tools

⅛ yard (11.4 cm) muslin

Strips of coordinating cotton fabrics, 1 to 4 inches (2.5 to 10.2 cm) wide and at least 4½ inches (11.4 cm) long.

2 strips of coordinating cotton fabrics, 1 to 2 inches (2.5 to 5 cm) wide and 9 to 11 inches (22.9 to 27.9 cm) long.

Coordinating rickrack in one or two colors

Cotton quilting thread, in white and in the colors of your rickrack

Double-sided fusible webbing

Decorative snaps and snap attachment device

SEAM ALLOWANCE

¼ inch (0.6 cm)

WHAT YOU DO

1 With a measuring tape, determine the measurement around your wrist at the desired tightness for the cuff. Add 1½ inches (3.8 cm) to this length to get the length of muslin you will need. For example, my wrist measurement is 8 inches (20.3 cm), so my muslin length is 9½ inches (24.1 cm).

2 Cut your muslin to the length you have determined, and then cut one piece from it 4½ inches (11.4 cm) wide and another 3 inches (7.6 cm) wide.

3 Place your 4½-inch (11.4 cm) muslin piece horizontally on your work surface. Lay out your cotton strips on it vertically in the order you wish to piece them in. Remembering that the strips will be sewn with a ¼ inch (0.6 cm) seam allowance, lay them out taking account of that loss of width. Lay out two or three pieces of rickrack between the strips as well.

4 When you have the strips and rickrack where you want them, trim them to the width of the muslin. Now you will begin the piecing. Move your strips of cotton off of your muslin, but keep them in the order you ave determined.

5 Start with the first strip on the left-hand side, and pin it, face up, to the left side of the muslin. Sew the right edge of that strip to the muslin ¼ inch (0.6 cm) from the strip's edge. Now take your second strip and pin it, top sides facing, directly on top of the first strip with their right edges aligned. Turn the muslin over, and sew a line to the left of your first, attaching the second strip to both the first and the muslin. Turn back over and press flat.

6 Continue to piece in this fashion, but sewing the strips together ¼ inch (0.6 cm) from the edge from the top instead of the bottom as you just did, until you have reached the end of your muslin.

ing strips on either side of the pre-pieced strip cut from your first pieced muslin. (See the photo, near left.)

10 When the second muslin is pieced, trim it like the first and then pin the two muslins together, top sides facing. Sew along the left, top, and right sides; backstitch at the beginning and end and at both corners, but leave the bottom edge open. Cut the top left and right corners to make it easier to turn out.

11 Turn inside out, pushing corners out, then press. Fold the bottom edge of both sides inward, pressing as you go. Make sure the sides align evenly. Cut a piece of double-sided fusible webbing 2 inches (5 cm) wide and ½ inch (1.3 cm) shorter than your cuff length.

12 Peel one side of the paper off. Stick the webbing, sticky side down, into the cuff, aligning the edge with the edge

7 Sew on the rickrack pieces through their centers, matching your thread to your rickrack so it will blend in. Turn your pieced muslin over and trim any overhanging strips, using the muslin and a ruler as your guide.

8 Measure 1½ inches (3.8 cm) down on your muslin width, and cut across the entire piece horizontally. This will leave you with two pieces of muslin, one 3 inches (7.6 cm) wide and one 1½ inches (3.8 cm) wide.

9 Take the 3-inch-wide (7.6 cm) muslin piece, and piece it using the same general technique as you did above. This time, run the strips horizontally, using the two longer coordinat-

of the ironed edge. Make sure the webbing is stuck down and unwrinkled, then peel the top layer of paper off. With your hands, press the cuff together, checking that the bottom ironed edges meet, and then iron according to the instructions for the fusible webbing.

13 Attach snaps to the right and left edges, using decorative snap covers on the back of both the male and female snaps.

PUTTING IT TOGETHER

The strips in this project are assembled using the foundation-piecing method.

autumn breeze

DESIGNER

LOUISE PAPAS

After composing this seasonal scene, you may be inspired to gather fabrics in different tones to complete a series of quilts. Spring Mist or Summer Wind, anyone?

WHAT YOU NEED

Basic sewing tools

22 inches (55.9 cm) cream cotton, such as quilter's muslin or homespun

10 inches (25.4 cm) autumnal floral print cotton

Fat sixteenth (22.9 x 27.9 cm) of light brown patterned cotton

Fat sixteenth (22.9 x 27.9 cm) each of small-print yellow, red, brown, and orange cotton

Cream thread

23½ inches (59.7 cm) cotton in a coordinating color for backing

23½ inches (59.7 cm) cotton batting

Perle embroidery thread in cream

6 inches (15.2 cm) orange-and-cream-striped cotton fabric for binding

SEAM ALLOWANCE

¼ inch (6 mm)

FINISHED SIZE

19 x 20 inches (48.3 x 50.8 cm)

WHAT YOU DO

1 To make the quilt top, cut the cream fabric to 21 x 20 inches (53.3 x 50.8 cm). It will be cut to size before the binding goes on so that the edges are neat.

2 Draw a set of tree top, tree trunk, and leaf patterns onto tracing paper and cut these out for templates.

3 Pin the tree top and tree trunk templates onto the appropriate floral and light-brown fabrics and cut one of each. Take the leaf template and cut 26 leaves from a mixture of the red, orange, yellow, and brown fabrics.

4 Using the photo as a guide, place the tree trunk in position on the quilt top and pin. Appliqué the tree trunk onto the quilt top using the cream thread. Repeat with the tree top.

5 Using the photo as a guide, place the leaves on the quilt and pin them into position. Appliqué them onto the quilt top.

6 Cut the backing fabric and batting 1 inch (2.5 cm) larger than the quilt top. Place the backing right side down and place the batting on top. Then place the quilt top onto the batting right side up. Smooth it down so there are no wrinkles, and pin through all the layers with safety pins.

7 Using the perle thread, quilt ⅛ inch (3 mm) away from the edge of the tree top, tree trunk, and leaves.

8 Using a washable marker or pencil, mark up the branch and trunk details and wind swirls. Quilt these lines using the perle thread.

9 Trim the quilt to measure 19 inches (48.3 cm) wide and 20 inches (50.8 cm) high.

10 Bind the quilt with your preferred method, using the orange-and-cream fabric.

book
nook

DESIGNER

MORGAN MOORE

What do bookworms, night owls, and children have in common? They all want this clever carrier! Slip your books and magazines into the canvas compartments when it's time to drift off to dreamland.

WHAT YOU NEED

Basic sewing tools

1 1/2 yards (137.2 cm) of canvas

2 1/2 x 15-inch (6.4 x 38.1 cm) piece of fabric to bind the larger pocket

1 1/2 x 11-inch (3.8 x 27.9 cm) piece of fabric to bind the smaller pocket

Four 4 1/2-inch (11.4 cm) squares of assorted fabrics for the letters

1/4 yard (22.9 cm) of paper-backed fusible web

WHAT YOU DO

1 Cut the canvas.

Piece A: 52 x 15 1/2 inches (132.1 x 39.4 cm)

Piece B: 14 1/2 x 15 1/2 inches (36.8 x 39.4 cm)

Piece C: 9 1/2 x 10 1/2 inches (24.1 x 26.7 cm)

2 Hem the long edges of canvas piece A by folding them under 1/4 inch (6 mm), pressing, folding them over again 1/4 inch (6 mm), and stitching.

3 To bind the top edge of the larger pocket, fold under both long sides of the larger pocket—binding fabric 1/4 inch (6 mm). Insert a shorter side of canvas piece B into one the folded edges (figure 1).

figure 1

Fold and pin the binding fabric so it conceals the edge of the canvas; then topstitch close to the edge and press. Stitch the opposite edge of the pocket trim to the canvas, stitching close to the trim's edge.

4 Using the C piece of canvas and the smaller piece of pocket trim, repeat step 3 to bind the edge of the smaller pocket.

5 Fold under the bottom of the smaller pocket—opposite the fabric binding—and the sides 1/4 inch (6 mm) and use pins to hold the folds. Pin the pocket to the center of the larger pocket and topstitch close to all edges but the top.

6 Fold under the sides and bottom of the large pocket ¼ inch (6 mm) and press. Pin the wrong side of the large pocket to one end of the right side of piece A, matching the edges (figure 2). Topstitch along the edge of the pocket to attach it to piece A. Set aside.

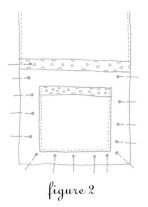

figure 2

7 Using a word-processing program, type the letters R, E, A, and D, and size the letters so they're 4 inches (10.2 cm) tall. Print them on heavy card stock and cut them out.

8 Follow the directions on the paper-backed fusible web to adhere it to the squares of fabric for the letters. Trace the card stock letters onto the fabric and cut them out. Remove the paper backing from the adhesive, position the letters on the canvas 3 inches (7.6 cm) from the top of the large pocket, and use a hot iron to attach them in place. Topstitch along the inner edge of the letters.

Place the finished cozy under your mattress. Sweet dreams!

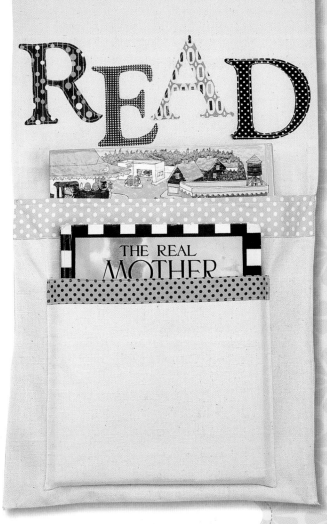

BED MATES

To make a cozy that hangs from both sides of the bed, repeat these directions to make another identical element. Sew both elements together along the unadorned side.

in bloom

$\mathcal{E}$mbroider your own garden, and watch it grow!
Mix and match your favorite flower shapes and colors
for a cheerful scene that brings a smile all day long.

DESIGNER
YVONNE EIJKENDUIJN

WHAT YOU NEED

Basic sewing tools

1 yard (.9 m) of white cotton for the pillow front and back

1 ¼ yard (1.1 m) of muslin for the pillow form

54 inches (1.4 m) of rickrack

16 inches (40.6 cm) of ⅜-inch (.95 cm) trim for the grass

Transfer pencil

Embroidery hoop

Embroidery floss in assorted colors for the flowers

Embroidery needle

Polyester fiberfill

SEAM ALLOWANCE

½ inch (1.3 cm) unless otherwise noted

FINISHED SIZE

16 x 10½ inches (40.6 x 26.7 cm)

What You Cut
White Cotton
- *1 rectangle, 11 x 16 inches (27.9 x 40.6 cm) for the pillow front*
- *2 rectangles, one 11 x 12 inches (27.9 x 30.5 cm), one 10 x 11 inches (25.4 x 27.9 cm) for the pillow back*

Muslin
- *2 rectangles, each 11 x 16 inches (27.9 x 40.6 cm)*

WHAT YOU DO

1 Copy the flower templates on page 291. Cut to separate the flowers, but do not cut them out. Cut out the fabric as described in the box, left. Decide how you want to arrange the flowers on the pillow front by mixing and matching them as desired. Trace the flowers with the transfer pencil, then press with an iron to transfer them to the pillow front.

2 With the fabric in an embroidery hoop, embroider the flowers to your liking. Use an assortment of floss colors to work stitches such as the satin stitch, chain stitch, straight stitch, backstitch, and split stitch. Lay the trim for the grass across the pillow front at the base of the flowers, pin, and stitch.

3 Center the rickrack over the front seam allowance. Pin the rickrack to the pillow front and baste.

4 On each piece cut for the back, turn one of the short sides under ¼ inch (6 mm) and press. Turn under once more to make a 1-inch (2.5 cm) hem, press, and sew. Finish the pillow with an envelope back.

5 Make the pillow form using the two pieces of muslin, stitching together with right sides facing. Leave an opening to turn and stuff. Stitch closed.

yard tale

Want to uproot the felt radishes and plant broccoli instead?
Removable felt pieces make it easy to change this quilt to suit your taste.

DESIGNER

ROXANNE BEAUVAIS

32

WHAT YOU NEED

Basic sewing tools

Templates (page 292–293)

Wool felt, 18 x 12-inch (45.7 x 30.5 cm) sheets, one light blue and one tan

Purple and tan thread

⅓ yard (30.5 cm) wood-grain fabric

Low-loft cotton batting, 20 x 17½ inches (50.8 x 44.5 cm)

Cotton backing fabric, 20 x 17½ inches (50.8 x 44.5 cm)

Wool felt, 9 x 12-inch (22.9 x 30.5 cm) sheets, in purple, blue green, dark blue, brown, gray, olive green, and yellow

Embroidery floss in yellow, gray, brown, blue green, olive green, red, orange, and white

Embroidery needle

Clear craft glue

SEAM ALLOWANCE

¼ inch (6 mm)

FINISHED SIZE

19¾ x 17¼ inches (50.2 x 43.8 cm)

WHAT YOU DO

1 Cut the light blue wool felt to 17¼ x 7¾ inches (43.8 x 19.7 cm). Cut the tan wool felt to 17¼ x 7¼ inches (43.8 x 18.4 cm). Sew the long ends of these two pieces together on a sewing machine with tan thread. Press the seam flat. This creates the sky and ground portions of the quilt top.

2 Cut four strips of the wood-grain fabric for the border in the following sizes:

- Two pieces, 19 x 2 inches (48.3 x 5.1 cm)

- Two pieces, 21¾ x 2 inches (55.2 x 5.1 cm)

3 Place the 19-inch (48.3 cm) strip of wood-grain fabric on the short, left side of the quilt top with right sides together. Center the strip, leaving a 1-inch (2.5 cm) overhang on either end. Starting ¼ inch (6 mm) in from the corner of the quilt, sew the wood-grain strip to the felt. Stop ¼ inch (6 mm) from the edge of the quilt. Following the same instructions, attach the other three strips to the corresponding edges of the quilt.

figure 1

4 Press all seams open. Turn the quilt over, create 45° angles at each corner, and press (figure 1). Unfold, match the pressed lines, and pin and sew. Be sure not to sew into the felt. Trim the excess and continue in this manner for the remaining corners. Press.

5 Sandwich the quilt layers— quilt top, batting, backing fabric. Carefully smooth out all layers and pin together using safety pins. As you add items and embroider the quilt, the pins may be removed.

6 Cut out felt pieces using the templates on page 292–293, or create your own clothing and vegetables in appropriate sizes. For the quilt shown here, you'll need a roof, door, treetop, tree trunk, garden plot, shirt, pants, and two each of carrots, onions, and radishes.

7 Cut a 6⅞-inch (17.4 cm) square from the blue-green felt for the house. Cut squares from the yellow wool felt for the windows in the following dimensions:

- Two 1⅛-inch (2.8 cm) squares
- One 1½ x 2-inch (3.8 x 5.1 cm) square

8 Cut a strip of dark blue felt ⅝ x 6⅞ inches (1.6 x 17.4 cm). Center the strip halfway down the felt house and sew it onto the house with purple thread. Place the purple roof piece on top of the house with a ¼-inch (6 mm) overlap and topstitch the roof and house together using purple thread on a sewing machine.

9 Apply the windows to the house using yellow embroidery floss and a running stitch by hand. Use a running stitch and gray embroidery floss to apply the door. Use the same floss to place a French knot on the door for a knob. Using a backstitch and brown embroidery floss, create the scalloped roof pattern, as shown on the template.

10 Apply the house to the quilt using a running stitch. Use gray embroidery floss on the house section and brown embroidery floss on the roof section.

11 Attach the garden pocket using brown embroidery floss and a running stitch. Start stitching on the short, right side, continuing across the bottom, up the left side and just around the curve. Leave the top flap open. Create rows in your garden by measuring 2 inches (5.1 cm) from either side of the pocket opening and stitching down the pocket to create three smaller sections.

12 Pin the green treetop to the quilt. Apply the tree trunk over it and stitch it down using brown embroidery floss and a running stitch. Apply a running stitch around the treetop with olive green embroidery floss.

13 Cut nine small round pieces for rocks from the gray felt. Using gray embroidery floss, stitch down the rocks to create a path from the front door to the garden. Each rock requires just a few stitches to hold it securely in place.

14 Stitch details on the clothes using various strands of embroidery floss. Apply a very small amount of clear craft glue to the knots on the back of each piece to secure them. Stitch details on the vegetables using a running stitch for the stems and a satin stitch for the vegetables. Use all strands of green, orange, red, and white floss accordingly. Again, apply a small amount of clear craft glue to secure the knots.

15 Apply the clothesline by making a French knot with the tan thread next to the house. Bring the thread back up and stretch it across the quilt to meet the tree. Leave a bit of sag in the thread. Bring the thread down and back up and make a French knot at the tree.

16 To make the binding, cut 80 inches (2 m) worth of 2½-inch (6.4 cm) wide strips of the wood-grain fabric. Attach the strips at an angle to create one long continuous strip. Fold the piece in half (right sides facing out) and press.

17 Starting several inches from a corner, lay the binding along the edge of the quilt with the raw edges matching up. Pin and sew. At the corners, stop ¼ inch (6 mm) from the edge. Fold the binding at an angle and start the next side ¼ inch (6 mm) in. Continue this all the way around, stopping several inches from your starting point. Connect your binding pieces, trim the excess, and then continue sewing the binding to the quilt.

18 Press the binding back. Pin in place and hand-stitch the binding to the back of the quilt.

CHANGE OF SEASONS

The photo above shows the house and garden without decoration. Make a variety of felt pieces to use when there's frost on the pumpkin or spring flowers are blooming.

soft spheres

DESIGNER
VALERIE SHRADER

$\mathcal{L}$ooking for that just-so Japanese zakka decorative accent?
Look no further than these elegant fabric balls.
Sew them up in multiples using Asian-inspired prints,
then display as a chic tablescape.

WHAT YOU NEED

Basic sewing tools

Fabric scraps

Thread to match

Polyester fiberfill

SEAM ALLOWANCE

¼ inch (6 mm) unless otherwise noted

FINISHED SIZE

3 x 3 inches (7.6 x 7.6 cm)
4 x 4 inches (10.2 x 10.2 cm)

WHAT YOU DO

1 Using the template on page 291, cut out six pieces, mixing the fabrics as desired.

2 Think of assembling your sphere from two pairs of three pieces each. To begin, stitch one edge of two pieces together, right sides facing. Fold the seam allowance back when you add the third piece, so you can see where the angles of the pieces align.

3 Make a second pair of three pieces as you did in step 2. Stitch each pair together, right sides facing, leaving an opening to stuff, and turn.

4 Stuff as desired. Use the slip-stitch to close the opening.

SUPERSIZE IT

You can enlarge or reduce the template as desired to change the size of the spheres.

*h*op in your step

You can never be too old (or young) to enjoy seeing a simple and charming scene hanging on the bedroom wall.

WHAT YOU NEED

Basic sewing tools

Light green cotton, one piece 8 x 3 inches (20.3 x 7.6 cm) and one piece 7 x 3 inches (17.8 x 7.6 cm)

Dark green cotton in these sizes: 10 x 2½ inches (25.4 x 6.4 cm), 12 x 2½ inches (30.5 x 6.4 cm), and 8 x 2½ inches (20.3 x 6.4 cm)

White cotton, one piece 7 x 9 inches (17.8 x 22.9 cm) and one piece 9½ x 12 inches (22.9 x 30.5 cm)

Embroidery floss in light green, dark green, brown, light brown, cream, and white

Batting, 9½ x 12 inches (24.1 x 30.5 cm)

Green bias tape, two 11-inch (27.9 cm) and two 14-inch (35.6 cm) pieces

SEAM ALLOWANCE

¼ inch (6 mm)

FINISHED SIZE

9½ x 12 inches (24.1 x 30.5 cm)

WHAT YOU DO

1 To make the front quilt piece, sew together the two light green and three dark green piece with the 7 x 9 inch (17.8 x 22.9 cm) white piece as shown in the photo. You'll need to cut a curve along the top of the shorter light green piece to make the hilltop.

2 Draw lines for the embroidery pattern with a fabric marker onto the quilt front and embroider the design with the floss.

3 Sandwich the quilt front, batting, and remaining 9½ x 12-inch (22.9 x 30.5 cm) white piece together and pin with safety pins, starting in the center. Quilt the layers together using the tying method, with bits of embroidery floss to match the fabric colors on the front. Make the knots at the back.

4 Sew the bias tape around the edge, folding in the corners.

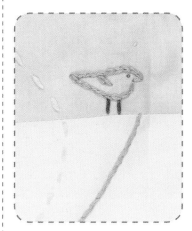

DESIGNER

AIMEE RAY

birdiemobile

DESIGNER

WENDY ARACICH

～

*T*his adorable patchwork mobile is a bright, cheery addition to any room. Felt wings are attached with a button for added movement, and the lightweight balsa support makes it easy to display.

WHAT YOU NEED

Basic sewing tools

¼ yard (22.9 cm) or 1 fat quarter each of three fabrics

5 yards (4.5 m) of ⅛-inch-wide (0.3 cm) ribbon

Thread

Wing template

6 assorted buttons, each ⅝ inch (1.6 cm)

Embroidery needle

Embroidery floss

Cotton or polyester stuffing

Remnant wool felt

Piece of balsa wood, ½ inch (1.3 cm) square and 18 inches (45.7 cm) long

SEAM ALLOWANCE

¼ inch (0.6 cm)

WHAT YOU DO

1 Cut 16 squares, each 2½ inches (6.4 cm), from all three fabrics. In a somewhat random pattern, arrange the squares on a work surface in a rectangle of seven columns and six rows.

2 Beginning with the first row, pin the right edge of the first square to the left edge of the second square with right sides together. Next, pin the right edge of the second square to the left edge of the third square. Continue pinning in this fashion until all squares in the top row are pinned. Set aside and repeat with remaining rows.

3 Machine stitch along pinned edges with a ¼-inch (0.6 cm) seam allowance. Press seams open. Join rows from top to bottom along common edges, taking care to

match the vertical seams. Press seams open.

4 On wrong side of the fabric, trace the large bird template four times and the small bird template two times. (See the templates on page 291). Cut the birds carefully along the traced line. Set scraps aside.

5 Cut three 2-inch (5.1 cm) pieces of ribbon. Fold one piece in half. Align the bottom edges of the ribbon with the top edge of one piece of the large bird (right side up), and pin in place. Place the corresponding bird piece on top, right sides together, and pin around edges, leaving the bottom open where indicated. Repeat with the two remaining birds.

6 Machine stitch around each bird with a ½-inch (1.3 cm) seam allowance, and leave the bottom open where indicated on the template. Trim seams, and turn right side out.

7 Pin the wings to the birds where indicated on the template. Place a button over the wing. With the embroidery needle and embroidery floss, sew the button to the wing, and make sure to go through both the wing and the top layer of the bird, but not the bottom layer of the bird. Repeat until all wings are attached.

8 Stuff the birds with stuffing. Tuck under seams of openings on each bird and pin. Close the opening by hand with a small running stitch.

9 Fold a saved scrap in half, right sides together, and pin to hold. With a pencil or dressmaker's chalk, draw a heart shape freehand on the fabric. Lay the cut heart on a piece of felt, and cut out one heart from the felt. Layer the felt heart between patchwork hearts, right sides out, and pin to hold. In the same fashion as the heart, make and cut two ovals and two leaves. Pin together with felt in the center.

10 Cut an 8-inch (20.3 cm) piece of ribbon, and sandwich it between the top and middle layers of the heart so the bottom of the ribbon is inside the heart, and the remainder extends out from the top of the heart. Embroider a running stitch from top to bottom through the center of the heart, taking care to catch the ribbon with the stitches. Next, embroider a running stitch from left to right through the center of the heart, taking care to catch the ribbon with the stitches.

11 Cut two 13-inch (33 cm) pieces of ribbon. Sandwich one ribbon between an oval, with about the same amount of ribbon extending out from the top and bottom of the oval. Stitch two rows of embroidery, one top to bottom and one left to right, taking care to catch the ribbon with your stitches. Repeat for the other oval.

OUT OF HARM'S WAY

For safety reasons, don't hang your mobile—with its enticing buttons—over a crib or other spot where it will be within reach of the busy hands (and mouths) of babies or toddlers.

12 Sandwich the end of the ribbon coming from an oval between a leaf, with the bottom of the ribbon inside the leaf. Attach the leaf to the ribbon as you did the ovals in step 11. Repeat for the other leaf.

13 Cut one 30-inch (75 cm) and two 26-inch (66 cm) pieces of ribbon. Thread one of the 26-inch pieces through the loop on one of the larger birds. Tie it to the wood support about two inches from the left end. Bring the ribbon around the support, and tie in a simple knot, leaving at least a 4-inch (10.2 cm) tail. Loop the ends down around the support, and tie a second knot beneath the support. Finally, bring the loops back around the top of the support, and tie in a bow. Trim excess ribbon if needed. Repeat with the remaining birds, tying the smaller bird in the center of the support and the other large bird around two inches from the right end.

14 Cut a 50-inch (1.25 m) piece of ribbon. Thread the ribbon from left to right under the ties on the wood support. Pull through to bring the ends together, and form a triangle. Tie the ends together with a knot and bow, and adjust to the desired length for hanging.

NO LUMBERJACK REQUIRED

You can find balsa wood in various sizes at your local craft store. A 1/2-inch-square (1.3 cm) piece will be thin and light enough that you can easily cut it to the required length with a utility knife.

obi*belt*

DESIGNER

BETHANY MANN

*T*ie your outfit all together with an obi belt. Traditionally used to tie a kimono or a martial arts uniform, this one features vintage ties in a knockout design.

WHAT YOU NEED

Basic sewing tools

Extra-wide vintage tie

4 x 15-inch (10.2 x 38.1 cm) scraps of 3 assorted fabrics

Coordinating thread

Paper bag or wrapping paper

Wool felt

Solid cotton backing fabric

2 yards (1.8 m) velvet ribbon, ¼ inch (0.6 cm) wide

SEAM ALLOWANCE

½ inch (1.3 cm)

WHAT YOU DO

1 Using your seam ripper, dismantle your vintage tie. Ties are cut in the bias, so cut the front panel from your tie by cutting on a diagonal to keep the grain of the fabric straight for your obi.

2 Determine your waist size. Cut the scraps of assorted fabrics into pieces that are 7 inches by 4 to 6 inches each (17.8 cm x 10.2 to 15.2 cm). Arrange the pieces in a symmetrical pattern to create a piece equal to your waist measurement. If your waist measurement is 28 inches (71.1 cm), for example, the total of the pieces would be 7 x 28 inches (17.8 x 71.1 cm).

3 Seam the patches together on the 7-inch (17.8 cm) edges to create a long, thin rectangle of patchwork. Press open all seams.

4 Cut a piece of paper bag 7 inches (17.8 cm) multiplied by half of your waist measurement. For example, if your waist measurement is 28 inches (71.1 cm), the piece of the paper bag would be 7 x 14 inches (17.8 x 35.6 cm). Fold the paper in half lengthwise, and draw a curved line from the top right corner to about halfway down at the left end. Keep the line as clean and flowing as possible.

MAKING ALLOWANCES

Don't forget about the ½-inch (1.3 cm) seam allowance! If made correctly, the quilted part of the belt should meet neatly in the back with no overlap or gapping.

5 Trim with scissors, and test fit by wrapping the piece around half your waist from belly button to backbone. If you notice gapping or crinkling, trim again, and fold in half to keep it symmetrical. This is your pattern.

6 Use your pattern (wider end on the fold) to trim your patchwork, and cut your wool felt for batting as well as your solid-color cotton backing piece. Trim the felt to 1/2 inch (1.3 cm) on each end.

7 Layer all the pieces in this order starting at the bottom: patchwork, right side up; solid backing, right side down; felt. Pin together, and then seam down both the long, curved sides.

8 Clip the curves. Then turn inside out and press, turning raw ends to the inside about 1/2 inch (1.3 cm). Topstitch 1/4 inch (0.6 cm) across the top and the bottom of the belt to stabilize it and help it lay flat.

9 Use your machine to stitch around some of the patterns printed on your patches. Work slowly, and don't get too detailed. You can use a contrasting thread in the bobbin to see your handiwork on the backside of the obi.

10 Pin the velvet ribbon in the center of each open end, and topstitch the opening closed as close to the edge as possible, but at least 1/4 inch (0.6 cm) from the end to make certain you catch all raw edges.

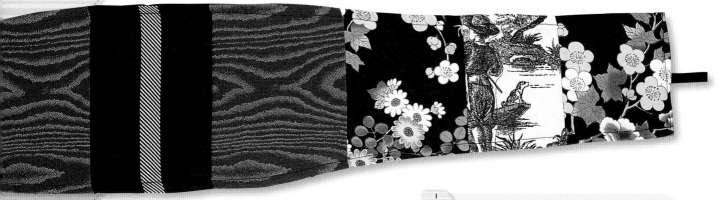

A FITTING DESIGN

This belt should be designed to lie wide and flat across your belly, curve over your hipbone, and stay straight around to the small of your back. It's made to fit your natural waist.

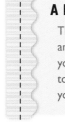

refab modern

Yesterday's fashion faux pas could be today's hottest home décor trend. There's a reason you've been holding onto that old sweater for so long. Don't part with it; repurpose it into this groovy felted pillow.

DESIGNER
LEESA RITTELMANN

WHAT YOU NEED

Basic sewing tools

Sweaters for felting made of at least 80% wool, I orange, I light pink, and I dark pink

Pair of denim jeans

1½ yard (1.4 m) of lightweight interfacing

7 x 25-inch (17.8 x 63.5 cm) piece of muslin

Rayon machine-embroidery thread in bright orange

Washing machine and clothes dryer

Rotary cutter and mat

I small bag of polyester fiberfill

SEAM ALLOWANCE

½ inch (1.3 cm) unless otherwise noted

FINISHED SIZE

12 x 6½ inches (30.5 x 16.5 cm)

What You Cut
Interfacing
- I rectangle, 3½ x 5½ inches (8.9 x 14 cm)
- I rectangle, 4½ x 7 inches (11.4 x 17.8 cm)
- I square, 6 inches square (15.2 cm)
- I rectangle, 7 x 8½ inches (17.8 x 21.6 cm)
- I strip, 3 x 7 inches (7.6 x 17.8 cm)

WHAT YOU DO

1 Felt the sweaters by washing them with the jeans in hot water—the jeans provide friction that aids the felting process.

2 Dry the sweaters in the clothes dryer on the *hottest* setting for 30 minutes or until fully dried and suitably felted.

3 Enlarge the template on page 291, and copy it. You may need to photocopy the template more than once in order to cut out multiple shapes, as the pillow front is a series of overlapping fabric blocks. Cut the interfacing as described in the box, left.

4 Cut the pieces for the pillow front. Pin template pieces 1 and 4 to the dark pink sweater and cut out. Pin templates 2 and 6 to the light pink sweater and cut out. Pin templates 3 and 5 to the orange felted sweater and cut out.

5 For the pillow back, cut a 7 x 10-inch (17.8 x 25.4 cm) piece from the dark pink felted sweater and a 7 x 8-inch (17.8 x 20.3 cm) piece from the orange felted sweater. One of the 7-inch (17.8 cm) sides on the orange piece should be a finished edge, such as a cuff or neckline. Set the pieces aside.

TEXTURAL INTEREST

Add a variety of textures to your pillow by felting sweaters made of cashmere, angora, mohair, cable knit, or plain knit merino wool.

6 You'll piece the two halves of the pillow front separately, starting with the left side. Place dark-pink piece 1 right side up on the 3½ x 5½-inch (8.9 x 14 cm) piece of interfacing. Lay light-pink piece 2 right side up on top of piece 1, aligning the lower left corners. Pin the layers in place.

7 Set your sewing machine for a close zigzag stitch. Sew along the smaller curve where piece 1 and 2 join, catching both fabrics with the stitch. Don't be concerned if the stitching causes the edges of the block to stretch, you'll be able to square it later.

8 Flip the layers over. Place your scissor ½ inch (6 mm) from the bottom left of the seam and carefully cut away both the interfacing and dark pink fabric to reveal the light pink shape below (figure 1). On the outside edge of the curved seam, cut only the interfacing, leaving a ¼-inch (6 mm) allowance around the seam (figure 2). The finished piece should resemble figure 3.

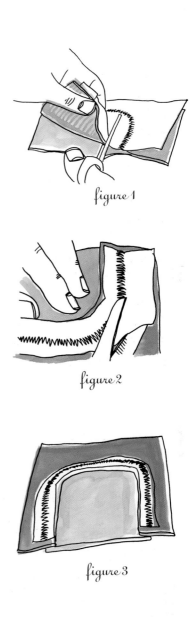

figure 1

figure 2

figure 3

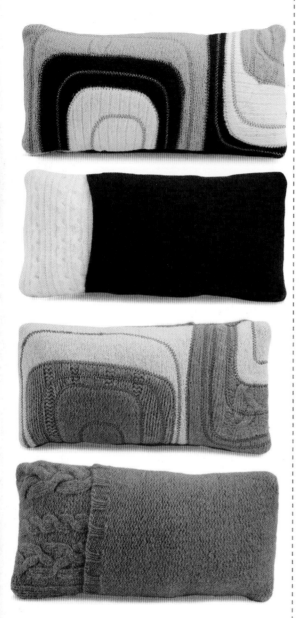

9 Place orange piece 3 right side up on the 4½ x 7-inch (11.4 x 17.8 cm) piece of interfacing. Lay the piece you made in steps 6–8 right side up over both pieces. Pin in place. Zigzag along the curved seam.

10 Make the right side of the pillow front. Lay dark-pink piece 4 right side up on the 6 inch (15.2 cm) square of interfacing. With straight edges aligned, position orange piece 5 on top, right side up and slightly off center. Pin the layers in place, and zigzag along the curved seam.

11 Flip the layers over and trim as you did in step 8. Trim the interfacing and dark pink fabric to reveal the orange shape below, then trim only the interfacing.

12 Position light-pink piece 6 right side up on the 7 x 8½-inch (17.8 x 21.6 cm) piece of interfacing. Lay the piece you made in steps 10–11 right side up on both layers. Center it, with top edges aligned. Pin, then zigzag along the curved seam.

13 Sew the halves of the pillow front together. Pin each side to the 3 x 7-inch (7.6 x 17.8 cm) strip of interfacing, keeping them as close as possible. Zigzag the seam where they join.

14 Use the grid on the cutting mat to square the pillow top to a 7 x 13-inch (17.8 x 33 cm) rectangle. Trim away any excess fabric with the rotary cutter.

15 With right sides together, pin the 7 x 10-inch (17.8 x 25.4 cm) piece you cut in step 5 for the pillow back to the left side of the pillow front with raw edges aligned. Make sure to position the finished edge inward. Sew the piece to the front.

16 Pin the 7 x 8-inch (17.8 x 20.3 cm) back piece right side down to the right side of the pillow and sew. When turned, the finished edge on the other back piece will overlap it. Clip the corners and carefully turn right side out. Gently push the corners out if necessary.

17 Fold the piece of muslin in half lengthwise with right sides together and press. Stitch, leaving an opening to turn and stuff. Stitch closed. Insert the form into the pillow.

DOUBLE UP

If you want to add a little more dimension to your decorative zigzag stitching, sew another line of zigzag over the first.

flowing scarf

$\mathcal{T}$his silk scarf is not about perfection; it's about improvisation. The fabrics used are notoriously tricky to sew, so don't fret over irregular seams. Let the fabrics do their thing, and just go with the flow.

DESIGNER

VALERIE SHRADER

WHAT YOU NEED

Basic sewing tools

Scraps of lightweight fabrics, such as silk chiffon, china silk, kimono remnants, and cotton batiste

Thread, neutral color

Decorative, variegated rayon thread, two complementary colors

SEAM ALLOWANCE

½ inch (1.3 cm)

WHAT YOU DO

1 Cut a series of strips from the scraps in varying widths, but none less than 2 inches (5.1 cm) wide. Construct seven 9 x 9-inch (22.9 x 22.9 cm) patchwork blocks by stitching them with the wrong sides together using the neutral thread. Trim each block to 8½ x 8½ inches (19 x 19 cm).

2 Embellish and finish the blocks by stitching the seam allowances down with one color of the rayon thread. Use a double strand to intensify the sheen and play with the color gradations. Vary your stitches if desired.

3 Stitch the blocks to one another using a ½-inch (1.3 cm) seam with either the right or wrong sides facing, as desired. Embellish the seam allowances as you did in step 2 with the second color of rayon thread.

4 Press under a narrow double hem along each of the long edges, pressing each hem to a different side of the scarf. Use a running stitch to secure the hem, sewing by hand and using the rayon thread of your choice. Repeat to hem the remaining short edges.

square deal

B locks of bold color, squiggly lines, and delicate French knots show that sometimes the simplest ideas are the best.

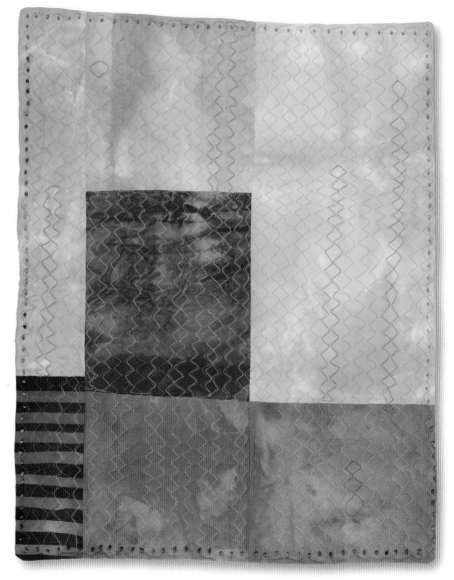

MALKA DUBRAWSKY

WHAT YOU NEED

Basic sewing tools

Template (page 289)

Note: All fabric is 44 inches (1.1 m) wide.

¼ yard (22.9 cm) raspberry cotton (piece 1)

¼ yard (22.9 cm) chartreuse cotton (pieces 2, 5, and 6)

¼ yard (22.9 cm) kelly green cotton (pieces 3 and 4)

⅛ yard (11.4 cm) raspberry-and-orange-striped cotton (piece 7)

Embroidery hoop

Turquoise embroidery thread

Embroidery needle

½ yard (45.7 cm) cotton batting

½ yard (45.7 cm) teal cotton for backing

Chartreuse thread

Machine-quilting thread in orange, turquoise, and white

SEAM ALLOWANCE

¼ inch (6 mm)

FINISHED SIZE

18 x 23 inches (45.7 x 58.4 cm)

WHAT YOU DO

1 Use a copier to enlarge the quilt template on page 289. Cut apart the seven pieces.

2 Pin piece 1 to the raspberry fabric and cut along the edges adding the ¼ inch (6 mm) seam allowance. Repeat with the other six template pieces, pinning them to their matching fabrics and cutting.

3 Sew pieces 1 and 2 together along their short edges. Press the seam to one side. It's best to alternate sides where seams intersect.

4 Following the template diagram, sew piece 3 to the strip containing pieces 1 and 2 along its long edge. Press to one side. Then sew pieces 4 and 5 together along their short edges. Press to one side.

5 Sew the strip containing pieces 4 and 5 to the strip containing pieces 1, 2, and 3 along the long edge. Press to one side.

6 Sew pieces 6 and 7 together along their short edges. Press to one side. Then sew the strip containing pieces 6 and 7 to the rest of the quilt top along the long edge.

7 With a ruler and pencil, mark the perimeter of the quilt top to place French knots, with knots about ½ inch (1.3 cm) from each edge and spaced ½ inch (1.3 cm) apart.

8 Place the quilt top in the embroidery hoop and, using turquoise embroidery thread, stitch French knots where marked. Reposition the embroidery hoop as needed.

9 Lay the batting on your cutting mat, and lay the teal backing fabric right side up on the batting. Lay the quilt top right side down on the backing and batting. Pin the layers together and trim them even.

10 Sew the layers together, leaving a 9-inch (22.9 cm) gap along one side. Trim the corners. Turn the quilt right side out, making sure to poke out the corners.

11 Press the quilt flat and turn under a ¼-inch (6 mm) seam allowance at the gap. Pin. Using chartreuse thread and a hand-sewing needle, slip-stitch the gap closed.

12 Lay the quilt on the cutting mat and baste with safety pins about every 4 inches (10.2 cm). Free-motion machine-quilt with an allover squiggle pattern in orange thread, removing pins as you go. Accent some of the squiggles by machine-quilting in white and turquoise.

COMBINATION PLATE

Can't find a striped fabric you like for the corner of the quilt? You can make your own striped fabric by seaming together strips of 1-inch (2.5 cm) wide fabric in shades of raspberry and orange (or the colors of your choice).

center of attention

Capture the glory of autumn year-round with this beautiful and simple design.

DESIGNER

RUTH SINGER

WHAT YOU NEED

Basic sewing tools

Leaf templates

Circles (such as embroidery hoops) to draw circles around

Cream cotton, 32-inch (81.3 cm) square

Pink cotton, 32-inch (81.3 cm) square

Cotton batting, 32 inches (81.3 cm)

18 scraps of prewashed fabric in different materials and textures, about 4 inches (10.2 cm) square each

¼ yard (22.9 cm) lightweight iron-on interfacing

Coordinating fabric scraps to make about 4 yards (3.6 m) of binding strips

Variegated embroidery thread for quilting

SEAM ALLOWANCE

None

FINISHED SIZE

18¼ inches (46.4 cm) square

WHAT YOU DO

1 To prepare the 18 leaves, first iron interfacing onto the back of the fabric scraps. Trace a different leaf design onto each scrap and cut out.

2 Arrange 17 leaves in a circular design about 16 inches (40.6 cm) in diameter on the cream fabric and pin. Put the last leaf in the center. Hand stitch the leaves into place using a matching sewing thread, or a contrasting embroidery thread if you prefer.

3 Draw the quilting lines shown in the photo with a fabric marker, using embroidery hoops or plates to create the circles. The center circles are 4 inches (10.2 cm), 9 inches (22.9 cm), and 13 inches (33 cm) in diameter. The corner circles are 5 inches (12.7 cm) and 3 inches (7.6 cm) in diameter.

4 Layer the quilt with the pink backing face down, then the batting, then the quilt top facing up. Use safety pins or baste in place.

5 Hand quilt the circles through all layers in large running stitches, using the embroidery thread. Start at the innermost center circle and work out. You can start and fasten the thread between the backing and the batting.

6 Remove the pins or basting and trim the quilt down to 28 inches (71.1 cm) square, cutting close to the corner stitching.

7 To make the binding, cut strips 2½ inches (6.4 cm) wide in a range of different fabrics to match or coordinate with the leaves. Join together to make a total length of about 4 yards (3.6 m).

8 Bind the quilt by your preferred method.

TREE HUGGING

It only makes sense in a quilt design that celebrates the diversity of nature: Organic cotton was used here in the quilt top, the backing, and the batting.

blue pools

*T*his combination of geometric shapes and free-form stitching is a snap to make. Dive right in!

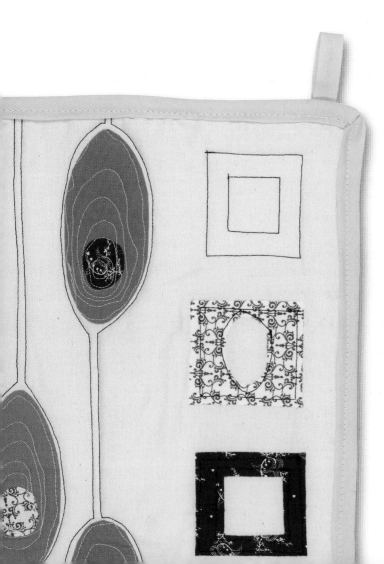

WHAT YOU DO

1 Cut the cream fabric to 10½ x 18½ inches (26.7 x 47 cm) and the batting and aqua fabric to 11 x 19 inches (27.9 x 48.3 cm).

2 Fuse a 4½ x 13-inch (11.4 x 33 cm) section of fusible web to the wrong side of the periwinkle fabric. Using a template you create or cutting freehand, cut six ovals that measure about 2 x 4 inches (5.1 x 10.2 cm).

3 Iron the ovals in place on top of the cream fabric, staggering the shapes to create three rows.

4 Fuse a 6 x 6-inch (15.2 x 15.2 cm) square of fusible web to the back of the light blue and dark blue print fabrics. From the light blue print, cut two 1-inch (2.5 cm) diameter circles and one 2½ x 2-inch (6.4 x 5.1 cm) rectangle. From the dark blue print, cut four circles and one rectangle using the same dimensions.

5 Cut an oval from the center of the light blue rectangle and a square from the inside of the dark blue rectangle.

6 Fuse the circles in place on top of the ovals. Baste the quilt top to the batting with pins, and free-motion stitch the shapes in place using cream thread. Start in the center of the circle and work your way out in oblong spirals. Once you have the ovals stitched down, you can unpin the layers.

7 Baste the top, batting, and backing together with pins and switch to blue thread. Using the photo as a guide, stitch up to and around each oval shape, working up the left side and down the right side of each row.

8 Working from the top right down, create a stitched 2-inch (5.1 cm) square (with a smaller square inside), fuse and then stitch the light blue print rectangle in place, and fuse and stitch the dark blue print rectangle in place. Create a row of four 5½-inch (14 cm) tall stitched rectangles of varying widths below the three rectangles.

9 Sandwich the quilt layers between the fold of the bias tape and topstitch the tape in place, going through all the layers at the same time. Cut two 3-inch (7.6 cm) lengths of bias tape, fold them both in half, and attach them along the top edge of the quilt to create hanging tabs.

A THINNER SANDWICH

It's a little easier to free-motion stitch the ovals in place through only the quilt top and the batting, but you could perform this step after all three layers (including the backing) are basted together. Doing it that way would display more stitching on the back of the quilt.

the elusive batiki bird

𝒴ou say you've never even heard of a batiki bird before?
Now that you've spotted one, it's time to make your own.

DESIGNER

SARAH ANN SMITH

WHAT YOU NEED

Basic sewing tools

4 pieces of white-on-white print, each 7 x 30 inches (17.8 x 76.2 cm)

1 piece of pale green-gray fabric, 5 x 30 inches (12.7 x 76.2 cm)

14 to 16 pieces of blue, teal, and green batiks, 2½ to 4 inches (6.4 to 10.2 cm) wide by 7 inches (17.8 cm) long

Fusible web, 9 x 12 inches (22.9 x 30.5 cm)

Hot pink/orange batik, 9 x 12 inches (22.9 x 30.5 cm)

Variegated embroidery floss in magenta/pink and orange/yellow

Embroidery needle and hoop

Cotton fabric for backing, 30 inches (76.2 cm) square

Cotton batting, 29 inches (73.6 cm) square

Quilting thread in complementary colors

½ yard (45.7 cm) batik or near solid for binding

SEAM ALLOWANCE

¼ inch (6 mm)

FINISHED SIZE

26½ inches (67.3 cm) square

WHAT YOU DO

CUTTING AND PIECING

1 To make the background, cut each white-on-white fabric into four long wedges; one wedge should be about 3½ inches (8.9 cm) on the wide end. Cut the remaining section into three pieces with the narrowest end no smaller than 1 inch (2.5 cm) wide.

2 Cut the pale green-gray fabric into three long wedges with the narrow end no narrower than about 1 inch (2.5 cm).

3 Lay out your strips, alternating fabrics. Turn so that approximately every other one the wide end of the wedge is at the top. Using a washable marking pen or pencil, number your strips at the very bottom from left to right so the order doesn't get confused while stitching.

4 Machine-piece six to eight strips to make the section to the left of the tree trunk about 8 to 9 inches (20.3 to 22.9 cm) wide. Machine-piece the remaining strips for the section to the right of the tree trunk. Press all seam allowances toward the tree trunk.

5 To make the tree trunk and branches, cut each small chunk of the blues, teals, and greens into two wedges. As you did with the background, alternate the wide end of the strips to create a stack of "logs" 30 to 32 inches (76.2 to 81.3 cm) long. Trim the edges and cut your tree trunk to be 3½ inches (8.9 cm) wide at the bottom and 2½ inches (6.4 cm) wide at the top.

6 Cut the remaining piece of fabric into two narrower strips, at least 1 inch (2.5 cm) wide on the narrow end, to use for the branches. Press all seam allowances in one direction.

INSTANT VARIETY

If you don't have an extensive stash, look for some fat quarters that have a lot of color variation in them, then "swiss cheese" cut chunks from various parts of the fat quarter to make it look like they were cut from different fabrics.

7 To piece the background to the tree, place your tree trunk so that it overlaps the two background pieces. Cut the background pieces along the edges of the tree trunk. Place the remaining two narrower strips of tree as branches. Divide the long strip on the left and use the remainder for the small upper branch on the right.

8 Using a washable marking pencil or pen, mark the outside edge of your branches. Remove the branch, then mark ½ inch (1.3 cm) inside this line. These inner (pink) lines will be your cutting lines (and not the outside line).

9 Piece your background as shown in the photo in this order. Sew the left branch to the upper and lower background pieces. Sew the small upper branch on the right to the small triangle of background and the center background section. Sew the larger branch on the right to the upper and lower portions of the background. Press the seams toward the branches so that the branches appear to be in front of the background.

CREATING THE APPLIQUÉ BIRD

10 Apply fusible web to the back of your bird fabric. Mark the outline of the bird (by copying the bird here or creating your own) and cut out. Position your bird using the quilt photo as a guide and fuse in place.

11 You can embroider the bird now or after you have quilted this piece. If you wait until later, the back of your embroidery stitches will show on the back of your quilt. You can embroider as you wish: The quilt pictured here uses strands of pink variegated and yellow-orange floss in different combinations, with a feather stitch for outlining and a straight stitch elsewhere. Whether you embroider before or after quilting, a hoop will keep the top flat as you stitch.

12 When the top is done, press and trim to 28 x 28 inches (71.1 x 71.1 cm). Make sure the overall impression of the background piecing and tree trunk is vertical, not tilted.

A PAINTER'S LIGHT

You can create a subtle sense of space by selecting light and dark shades of the same color for your quilting and arranging them to make it appear the light is coming from one direction. For example, the tree trunk here uses a medium-dark blue on the left side for the contour lines, and a brighter aqua on the right side, the side of the light source.

LAYERING AND QUILTING

13 Place your backing fabric face up on the table, then the batting, and finally your neatly pressed top. Baste using your favorite method.

14 Hand- or machine-quilt the piece. First, quilt in the ditch (on the background side of the piecing lines, right next to the seam line) around the tree trunk and branches.

15 When the quilting is complete, square up your quilt to 26½ inches (67.3 cm) square.

BINDING

16 Use the method of binding you prefer. This quilt was made with a bias-double-fold binding for strength and sturdiness. To make this binding, first cut bias strips 3½ inches (8.9 cm) wide. You will need about 110 running inches (2.8 m) of bias.

17 Sew the strips together and press the seams open. Fold the bias in half and sew to your quilt, finishing the ends and sewing down using the technique you like best.

quick change

$\mathcal{P}$resto chango! When you want to change this pillow,
simply unhook the elastic, reverse the flaps by turning them to the other
side of the pillow, and hook them to the button on the other side.

WHAT YOU NEED

Basic sewing tools

½ yard (45.7 cm) of fabric A, a light print for the pillow back

½ yard (45.7 cm) of fabric B, a dark print for the pillow top
¼ yard (22.8 cm) each of four different light cotton prints

¼ yard (22.8 cm) each of four different dark cotton prints

1 package of 1-inch (2.5 cm) piping

20 inches (50.8 cm) of 2 mm black elastic cord

½ yard (45.7 cm) of batting

Polyester fiberfill

2 black ¾-inch (1.9 cm) shank buttons

Black embroidery floss

Embroidery needle

Zipper foot

SEAM ALLOWANCE

½ inch (1.3 cm) unless otherwise noted

FINISHED SIZE

12 x 12 inches (30.5 x 30.5 cm)

WHAT YOU DO

1 Enlarge the template on page 293 and cut it out. Use it to cut out eight triangles, one each from the four light cotton prints, and one each from the four dark cotton prints. Pair the triangles, one light with one dark. These will become the reversible flaps of the pillow.

2 Cut a 13-inch (33 cm) square, one each from fabric A and fabric B.

3 Cut four pieces of piping, each 20 inches (50.8 cm) long. Cut four pieces of the black elastic cord, each 5 inches (12.7 cm) long.

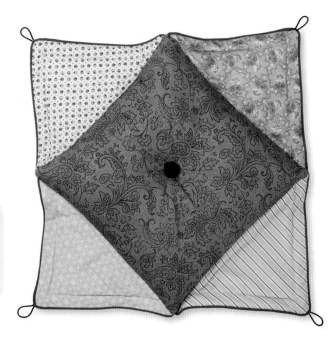

4 With raw edges aligned and right sides up, pin a piece of piping around the two short sides of one triangle of a pair. Stitch the piping to the triangle using the zipper foot on your machine.

FEEL GOOD

For a truly dynamic look and feel, consider using fabrics with different textures on each flap. For example, try: flannel, linen, wool, or fleece.

5 Fold one of the elastic pieces in half. Lay the elastic on the piping at the tip of the triangle, aligning the raw ends of the elastic with the raw edges of the seam allowance (figure 1). The loop of elastic will be pointing to the base of the triangle. Pin and sew.

figure 1

6 Lay the other triangle from the pair on its mate, right sides together. Pin along the edges with the piping. With the zipper foot on your sewing machine, stitch them together. Turn right side out, and press flat. Repeat steps 4–6 on the remaining pairs of triangles.

7 Cut four triangles out of the batting. As these triangles need to be shorter than the fabric triangles, trim 1 inch (2.5 cm) off the base of the triangle pattern before cutting.

8 Lay one batting triangle inside each flap, push it snug into the point, and pin in place. Topstitch the triangles ¾ inch (1.9 cm) in from the edges all the way around.

9 Lay the square of fabric A right side up on your work surface. Lay the flaps with dark sides down on top of the square. Align the raw edges. The tip of each triangle with the elastic loop should be pointing toward the center of the square. Use a ¼-inch (6 mm) seam allowance around all edges to baste in place.

10 Place the square of fabric B on top of the square of fabric A with flaps right sides together. Pin through all layers. Machine-stitch around the edges, leaving a 5-inch (12.7 cm) opening for turning. Trim the corners and turn the piece right side out.

11 Use the fiberfill to stuff the pillow. Turn the edges of the opening under, and stitch closed.

12 Use the embroidery needle and the black embroidery floss to attach the buttons, one on either side of the pillow. Stitch tightly.

13 Hook the elastic loops around the button.

that's amore

$\mathcal{W}$hat is love?
To some, it's in the perfect
meal. To others, it's in the
details—like the small
heart buttons, dainty
stitching, and delicate
patchwork of this
oversize hot pad.

DESIGNER

KAREN WITTKOP

WHAT YOU NEED

Basic sewing tools

2 pieces of fabric for the front and the back, each 11 inches (27.9 cm) square

Medium-weight iron-on interfacing, 10½ inches (26.7 cm) square

2 different fabrics for the hills, each 7 x 9 inches (17.8 x 22.9 cm)

Fabric for the water, 11 x 3½ inches (27.9 x 8.9 cm)

5 x 11-inch (12.7 x 27.9 cm) piece of sheer tissue paper

Fabric for the bird, 3 x 4 inches (7.6 x 10.2 cm)

Fabric for the bird's wing, 2½ x 2 inches (6.4 x 5.1 cm)

2 scraps paperback fusible webbing, 3 x 4 inches (7.6 x 10.2 cm) for the bird and 2½ x 2 inches (6.4 x 5.1 cm) for the wing

Chalk pencil

Pinking shears

2 separated strands of black embroidery floss

Embroidery needle

6 small heart-shaped buttons in blue, green, and purple

Dense, thin cotton batting, 10½ inches (26.7 cm) square

6 inches (15.2 cm) of lavender rickrack

Black acrylic paint

Toothpick

SEAM ALLOWANCE

¼ inch (0.6 cm) except as otherwise noted

WHAT YOU DO

1 Cut all fabrics according to the materials list. Center and fuse the iron-on interfacing to the back of one of the squares; this will be the front.

2 Place the 7 x 9-inch (17.8 x 22.9 cm) pieces of fabric face up, and use the chalk pencil to draw free-form hill shapes on them, starting at the top corner and ending about 2 inches (5.1 cm) up from the opposite bottom corner. One piece should go left corner to right, and the other right corner to left. Cut along the lines with the pinking shears.

3 Pin the left-hand-side hill to the front, right side up, and topstitch along the pinked edge just below your cutting line. Repeat on the right side with the other hill.

4 Place the 11 x 3½-inch (27.9 x 8.9 cm) piece of fabric wrong side up, and draw a free-form scalloped edge for the water. Cut along the marked line with the pinking shears. Pin the water, right side up, over the hills at the bottom of the front and topstitch.

5 Using a water-soluble marker, sketch the word "Amore" in your best cursive.

With two strands of embroidery floss threaded in the needle, use a small, even running stitch, to embroider it.

6 Fuse the paper-backed fusible webbing to the backs of the fabrics chosen for the bird and the wing. Copy the templates from

USABLE FUSIBLE

Follow the manufacturer's instructions in applying fusible materials.

page 295, pin them to the fabric, and cut them out.

7 Remove the backing of the fusible web from the bird and the wing, and place the pieces in position on the front. Iron to fuse them down. Slowly topstitch around the edges, using short stitches. Sew on the buttons in a design that appeals to you.

8 Place the batting on your work surface, and center the unembellished square for the back over it, right side up. Layer the front, wrong side up, on top of that, and pin all around. Stitch around the edges, leaving a 4-inch (10.2 cm) opening in one edge for turning. Clip the corners, trim any batting that extends past the stitch-ing, and turn right side out. Finger-press the project flat, and push out the corners. Neatly fold in the seam allowance in the opening, and press. Fold the rickrack in half, and insert the cut edges into the opening, centering it, to serve as the hanging loop. Pin in place.

9 Topstitch around the entire hot pad, 1/8 inch (0.3 cm) from the edge. To reinforce it, topstitch twice over the insertion spot for the rickrack.

10 Dip the toothpick in the black paint, and dab on the eye of the bird.

THINK PINK

Leaving a raw, pinked edge will allow the hills to fray a little bit when washed, which adds an appealing texture.

airborne appliqué

𝓕lying dreams are the sweetest. Let this little work of avian-inspired art send you soaring to slumberland with wings outstretched.

DESIGNER
KAJSA WIKMAN

WHAT YOU NEED

Basic sewing tools

½ yard (45.7 cm) of linen for the pillow front

½ yard (45.7 cm) of checkered cotton for the pillow back

½ yard (45.7 cm) of a solid cotton for the pillow back

½ yard (45.7 cm) of muslin for the pillow form

Paper-backed fusible web

Fabric scraps for the bird appliqués

Black cotton machine-embroidery thread

Appliqué foot (optional)

Water-soluble fabric marker

Darning foot

Orange embroidery floss

Embroidery needle

Thread to match

Button

Polyester fiberfill

SEAM ALLOWANCE

¼ inch (6 mm) unless otherwise noted

FINISHED SIZE

12 x 12 inches (30.5 x 30.5 cm)

What You Cut

Linen
- 1 square, 12 ½ inches (31.8 cm) square for the pillow front

Checkered Cotton
- 1 rectangle, 9 ½ x 12 ½ inches (24.1 x 31.8 cm) for the pillow back

Solid Cotton
- 1 rectangle, 9 ½ x 12 ½ inches (24.1 x 31.8 cm) for the pillow back

Muslin
- 2 squares, each 12 ½ inches (31.8 cm) square for the pillow form

WHAT YOU DO

1 Trace the templates on page 293. Cut the fabric as described in the box, left. Transfer a reverse image of the traced templates to the paper-backed fusible web. Cut the birds out of the fusible web, leaving a ¼-inch (6 mm) allowance around each shape.

2 Select the fabric scraps you want to use for the birds. Fuse each piece of cut webbing to the wrong side of a fabric scrap. Trim the ¼-inch (6 mm) allowance away.

3 Decide where you want to place the bird appliqués on the linen square. Peel the paper backing off and press to fuse them to the front.

4 Thread your sewing machine with the machine-embroidery thread, and change to an appliqué foot if you have one. Set the machine for a short, straight stitch. Topstitch around the edges of the appliqués. Sew the beaks and feet of the birds at the same time (figure 1). **Note:** You may find it helpful to draw the beaks and feet first using a water-soluble marker.

figure 1

LIGHTEN UP

You can easily change the look of the pillow by using a white fabric for the front and bright fabric scraps for the bird appliqués.

5 Set your machine for free-motion stitching by dropping the feed dogs and changing to the darning foot. Write your text on the pillow front with the soluble marker. Stitch the text in free motion.

6 Thread the embroidery needle with two strands of the orange floss. Fill in just one of the bird's beaks using seed stitches.

7 Make an envelope back for the pillow. Hem one of the long sides on each of the rectangles cut for the pillow back. Turn the edges under ½ inch (1.3 cm) and press. Turn under again 1 inch (2.5 cm) and press. Make a buttonhole, centering it on the hem of the checkered fabric.

8 Pin the back piece with the buttonhole to the front first—when you turn the pillow you want the buttonhole on top—and sew. Use a zigzag stitch to overcast the seams. Sew on the button.

9 Make the pillow form from the muslin squares, stitching together with right sides facing. Leave an opening to turn and stuff; stitch closed. Insert the form into your pillow.

MORE THAN YOU KNOW

Recycle men's shirts for the pillow back. You'll be surprised how much fabric you can get out of just one. Thrift stores are a great source for old shirts in vintage fabrics.

bonbon brooches

DESIGNER

JENNIFER COOKE

$\mathcal{P}$illows don't just comfort your body—they can decorate it, too. Make a bold fashion statement with these scrap-busting brooches in eye-catching colors and contrasting thread.

WHAT YOU NEED

Basic sewing tools

Cotton fabric scraps

Batting scraps

Thread to match or contrast

Metallic thread (optional)

Tailor's chalk or water-soluble fabric marker

Polyester fiberfill

Metal pin back

SEAM ALLOWANCE

¼ inch (6 mm) unless otherwise noted

FINISHED SIZE

1 x 1½ inches (2.5 x 3.8 cm)

WHAT YOU DO

1 Copy the template on page 310 and cut it out. For the front of the pin, cut 2-inch (5.1 cm) squares from two different fabric scraps. For the back of the pin, cut two strips from the same solid-color fabric scrap, one 2 x 4 inches (5.1 x 10.2 cm) and one 2½ x 4 inches (6.4 x 10.2 cm). You'll trim these strips later, so you don't need to be exact when cutting.

2 Stitch the two front pieces together along one edge. Press the seams to one side, either right or left.

3 Cut the quilt batting to the same size as the stitched front. Lay the front right side up on top of the batting. Sew straight lines, approximately ⅛ inch (3 mm) apart, to quilt the top.

4 For the back of the pin, fold one of the long edges on the wider strip under ¼ inch (6 mm) and press. With right sides up, overlap the raw edge on the narrower strip with the folded edge on the other strip and pin.

ONE OF A KIND

Experiment by creating your own pin template to alter the shape. For even more fun, quilt the top using free-form machine stitching—just drop the presser foot to swirl and twirl the fabric at will.

5 With right sides facing, lay the front of the pin on the back. Center the template on the fabric, and trace around it using tailor's chalk or a water-soluble fabric marker.

6 Using the traced line as your stitching guide, sew through all layers of fabric. Backstitch as you complete the oval. Trim the seam. Clip the curves carefully—take small snips!

7 Turn the pin right side out through the opening on the back and press. Stuff the pillow with the fiberfill. A tapestry needle or chopstick is helpful for stuffing small items.

8 Hand-stitch the back of the pin closed along the folded edge. Center the metal pin back on the seam and sew it to the back.

A LITTLE BLING

Use metallic thread for the decorative stitching. Since it has a tendency to break under tension, only use the metallic thread for the bobbin. Thread the top of the machine with a matching color of regular thread and stitch with the wrong side up. The shiny metallic will appear on the front of your pin.

cuddle drops

Made using invitingly soft fleece and super sweet, candy-colored, recycled fabrics, these plush pillows are cuddle ready. Perhaps their contentedly closed lids will inspire you to indulge in a little snooze.

DESIGNER

ELLEN WRIGHT-SHAW

WHAT YOU NEED

Basic sewing tools

⅓ yard (30.2 cm) of fleece fabric for the drop

Scrap of recycled vintage/retro fabric for the face

Scrap of black felt

Thread to match

1 decorative button

Polyester fiberfill

SEAM ALLOWANCE

¼ inch (6 mm) unless otherwise noted

FINISHED SIZE

8 x 12 inches (20.3 x 30.5 cm)

WHAT YOU DO

1 Cut two teardrop shapes from the fleece. Copy or trace the face template on page 295: cut one face from the recycled vintage/retro fabric. Cut two eyelids from the scrap of black felt.

2 Place the face right side up on one of the fleece drops, centering it on the lower part of the drop (figure 1). Using plenty of pins to keep the shape from shifting when you stitch, pin inside the shape as well as around the edges.

figure 1

80

3 For a wide, bold line of stitching, set your machine for a wide, short zigzag. Sew around the edge of the circle. Then set your machine for straight stitching. Stitch two lines around the circle, outlining the zigzag stitch. Stitch one line on the outside of the zigzag, stitching over the points, then stitch another inside the zigzag. Set your iron to medium and press around the stitching.

4 Pin the eyelids to the face, and then edgestitch them around all edges. At the right eyelid, sew three straight lines coming diagonally off the side of the lid (figure 2). Drop your feed dogs to free-motion embroider a small circle at the end of each line. Position the button at the upper left of the other eyelid and sew.

5 Pin the two pieces of fleece right sides together and sew. Leave a 3-inch (7.6 cm) opening at the bottom of the drop for turning. Overcast the seam using a zigzag stitch.

6 Turn right sides out and stuff with the fiberfill. Stuff until firm, adding small handfuls at a time and shaping as you go. Hand-stitch the opening closed.

FOLLOW THAT THREAD

Wondering where to find great old fabrics? Search your own closets and cupboards first. Look for pillowcases, bedspreads, table cloths, and clothing. To extend your quest, visit local resale shops, yard sales, and flea markets.

figure 2

Two endless rows of triangles circle around delicate embroidery in this classic quilt.

WHAT YOU NEED

Basic sewing tools

¾ yard (68.6 cm) white cotton

Assorted fabrics in bright colors, enough for 28 squares, each 2⅜ inches (6.1 cm)

Green embroidery floss

Thin cotton batting, 23 x 18 inches (58.4 x 45.7 cm)

¼ yard (22.9 inches) green cotton for binding

SEAM ALLOWANCE

None

FINISHED SIZE

15 x 21 inches (38.1 x 53.3 cm)

DESIGNER

DORIE BLAISDELL SCHWARZ

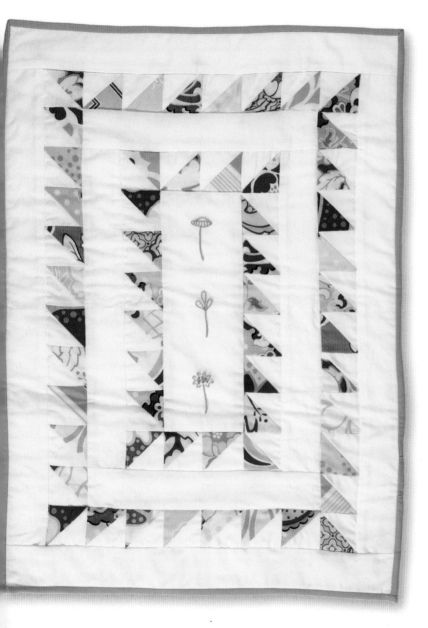

1 From the white cotton, cut the following pieces:

- One 23 x 18 inches (58.4 x 45.7 cm)

- 28 2⅜-inch (6.1 cm) squares

- One 9½ x 3½ inches (24.1 x 8.9 cm)

- Two 12½ x 2 inches (31.8 x 5.1 cm)

- Two 9½ x 2 inches (24.1 x 5.1 cm)

- Two 18½ x 2 inches (47 x 5.1 cm)

- Two 15½ x 2 inches (39.4 x 5.1 cm)

2 From the brightly colored fabrics, cut 28 2⅜-inch (6.1 cm) squares.

3 On the wrong side of each colored 2⅜-inch (6.1 cm) square, mark a line using a straight edge and pencil that goes diagonally across the square, from one point to its opposite point.

4 Bring together one white square and one colored square and line them up, right sides facing. Sew them together by sewing ¼ inch (6 mm) on each side of the diagonally drawn line. Repeat with the rest of the squares.

5 Cut the squares on the pencil line. Each sewn square becomes two half-square triangle units. Press the triangles open into squares, pressing the seams toward the colored fabric.

6 You now have all the pieces for the quilt top. Lay them all out so that they match the layout of the quilt in the photo. Pay careful attention to the direction of the triangle slant on each corner.

7 Starting with the rows around the center, sew the half-square triangles to each other, forming strips. You'll have two strips of six half-square triangle units, two strips of four half-square triangle units, two strips of ten half-square triangle units, and two strips of eight half-square triangle units.

8 Sew the six unit strips to the long sides of the 9½ x 3½-inch (24.1 x 8.9 cm) rectangle. Sew the four unit strips to the short side. Continue to build out from the center in this way. Next sew the 12½ x 2-inch (31.8 x 5.1 cm) white rectangles to the long side of the center, then add the 9½ x 2-inch (24.1 x 5.1 cm) white rectangles, and so on, until you have finished the top.

9 Embroider the motifs in the center using two strands of the green floss. The quilt shown here includes plant motifs with stem stitch for the stems, lazy daisy stitch for the lowest flower's petals, French knots for its center, and backstitch for the rest.

10 Make the quilt sandwich with white cotton on bottom, cotton batting in the middle, and the quilt top on top. Use safety pins to baste through all the layers

11 Quilt the quilt by "stitching in the ditch"—stitch along all the seam lines of all the rectangles. Start in the middle and work your way out.

12 Bind the quilt using ¼-inch (6 mm) binding.

spinning in orbit

*T*hink globally as you assemble this composition of rectangles, squares, and circles.

WHAT YOU NEED

Basic sewing tools

Template (page 295)

½ yard (45.7 cm) each of
8 different cotton fabrics

Template plastic

Permanent marker

Batting, 36 x 31 inches (.9 x .8 m)

Backing fabric, 36 x 31 inches
(.9 x .8 m)

Needles for hand sewing and
hand quilting

Cream embroidery floss

10 inches (25.4 cm) of 44-inch
(1.1 m) wide fabric for binding

SEAM ALLOWANCE

¼ inch (6 mm), unless otherwise
noted

FINISHED SIZE

33½ x 28½ inches (85 x 72.4 cm)

DESIGNER

KATE HENDERSON

WHAT YOU DO

1 Cut your eight fabrics to pieces in the following sizes:

- **Fabric A:** one 8½ inches (21.6 cm) x 28½ inches (72.5 cm) and one 6½ inches (16.5 cm) square

- **Fabric B:** one 10½ inches (26.7 cm) x 10 inches (25.4 cm) and one 5½ inches (14 cm) square

- **Fabric C:** one 10½ inches (26.7 cm) x 10 inches (24.5 cm) and one 5½ inches (14 cm) square

- **Fabric D:** one 10½ inches (26.7 cm) x 10 inches (24.5 cm)

- **Fabric E:** one 7½ inches (19 cm) x 28½ inches (72.5 cm) and one 4½ inches (11.4 cm) square

- **Fabric F:** 8½ inches (21.6 cm) x 17½ inches (44.5 cm) and one 4½ inches (11.4 cm) square

- **Fabric G:** one 4½ inches (11.4 cm) x 11½ inches (29.2 cm)

- **Fabric H:** one 4½ inches (11.4 cm) x 11½ inches

(29.2 cm) and one 6½ inches (16.5 cm) square

2 Following the photo with labels on page 87, sew as follows, ironing each seam as you go:

- Sew B to C and C to D along the 10½-inch (26.7 cm) edge.

- Sew G to H along the 11½-inch (29.2 cm) edge and then to F along the 8½-inch (21.6 cm) edge.

- Sew A to the B-C-D strip sewn above. Sew the other edge of B-C-D to E.

- Finally, sew E to the F-G-H strip sewn above.

3 Copy the template on page 295 and use the template plastic and a permanent marker to make three circle templates. You'll use these to cut circles from the square pieces of cut cloth. To do this, center the appropriate template over the right side of the fabric and trace around the circle with a fabric marker. Cut ¼ inch (6 mm) outside of the traced line. Match circle templates to squares as follows:

- Use the 3½-inch (8.9 cm) template for the 4½-inch (11.4 cm) squares of E and F.

- Use the 4½-inch (11.4 cm) template for 5½-inch (14 cm) squares of B and C.

- Use the 5½-inch (14 cm) template for the 6½-inch (16.5 cm) squares of A and H.

4 Press along the traced lines with your finger and pin the circles to the background, referring to the finished quilt picture for placement. Using thread to match the circle, slipstitch the circles to the background, tucking under the

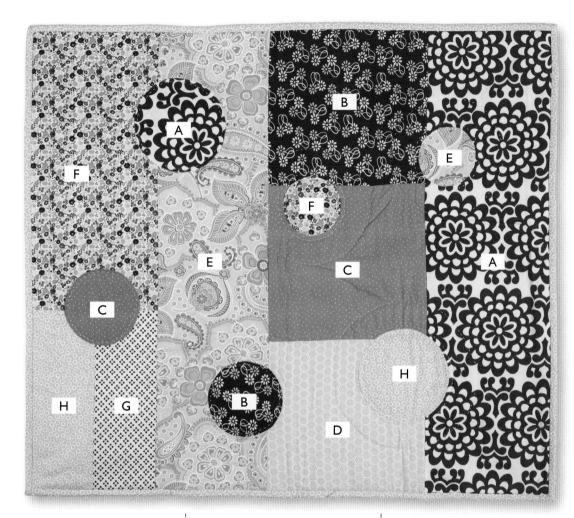

seam allowance with your needle as you go. Spray the circles with water to remove the marker.

5 Layer the quilt top, batting, and backing. Baste with safety pins or big running stitches.

6 Using two strands of cream embroidery floss and a needle, quilt ¼ inch (6 mm) inside the circles and then ¼ inch (6 mm) outside the circles and 1¾ inches (4.4 cm) outside the circles. Remove the safety pins.

7 Cut the binding fabric into four strips, each 2½ inches (6.4 cm) wide. Join and press the seams open. Press the strip in half along the length. Trim the backing and the batting and bind the quilt, mitering the corners.

spiffypotholders

DESIGNER

WENDY ARACICH

*C*an't take the heat? Stitch up these fun, vintage-inspired potholders to add some pizzazz to your kitchen. Embroidered blanket-stitching and patchwork piping add an extra dash of adorable.

WHAT YOU NEED

Basic sewing tools

1/4 yard (22.9 cm) or a fat quarter each of four fabrics (two shades of pink and two of yellow)

1/4 yard (22.9 cm) white cotton

White thread

Remnant green fabric

1/8 yard (11.4 cm) paper-backed fusible web

Pink and yellow embroidery floss

Embroidery needle

2 yards (1.8 m) of cord for piping

1/4 yard (22.9 cm) insulated batting

SEAM ALLOWANCE

1/4 inch (0.6 cm)

WHAT YOU DO

1 Cut ten 2 1/2-inch (6.4 cm) squares of each yellow fabric for a total of 20 yellow squares. Cut nine 2 1/2-inch (6.4 cm) squares of light pink fabric and eight 2 1/2-inch (6.4 cm) squares of dark pink fabric for a total of 17 pink squares. Cut four 7 1/2 x 7 1/2-inch (19 x 19 cm) squares of white cotton. Cut two 7 1/2 x 7 1/2-inch (19 x 19 cm) squares of insulated batting.

2 Arrange the 2 1/2-inch (6.4 cm) squares on a work surface, yellow in three columns and four rows and pink in three columns and three rows. Arrange the squares in an "every other" pattern with an equal amount of each fabric. Set aside the remaining 16 squares (eight yellow and eight pink).

3 For each grouping of squares, beginning with the first row, pin the right edge of the first square to the left edge of the second square with right sides together. Next, pin the right edge of the second square to the left edge of the third square. Set aside, and repeat with remaining rows.

4 Machine stitch along pinned edges. Press seams open. For each grouping of squares, join rows from top to bottom along common edges, and be sure to match seams. Press seams open.

5 On the wrong side of the fabric, trace the banana template on yellow patchwork and the strawberry template on pink patchwork. Trace the strawberry leaf template on green fabric (see the templates on page 294). Adjust the template placement to determine composition of patchwork within the shape. Cut out the shapes carefully along the traced lines.

6 Pin the fruit shapes to the fusible web, right side up, and slowly cut out. Remove pins, and iron fabric to web following the manufacturer's instructions.

7 Remove the strawberry's paper backing, and place the strawberry where you wish on white fabric, right side up. Iron to fuse the strawberry to the white fabric. Then place the leaf where you wish on top of the strawberry and white fabric, and iron to fuse. Repeat with the banana on a separate piece of white fabric.

8 With the pink embroidery floss, sew a blanket stitch around the perimeter of the strawberry and leaf. With the yellow embroidery floss, sew a blanket stitch around the perimeter of the banana. Then using embroidery floss and a simple backstitch, freehand "fraise" on the strawberry potholder and "platano" on the banana.

9 Arrange the remaining squares in two rows, one of pinks and one of yellows, in an "every other" pattern. Working from left to right, seam together squares to form rows. Press seams open. Then cut each row in half lengthwise. Pin two strips together end to end, and stitch to create a longer strip. Press seams open. Repeat with the other row.

10 Cut two 32-inch (80 cm) pieces of piping cord. Lay on top of the patchwork rows, right side down, and center the cord (figure 1). Fold in half, wrong sides together. Pin along the inside of the cord and stitch.

11 Align the raw edge of the piping with the edge of the potholder front, and pin along the stitched line, curving the piping at the corners and overlapping at ends; trim away any excess cord if necessary before you overlap the ends. Stitch along the seamline.

12 Cut two 2½ x 4½ (6.4 x 11.4 cm) pieces of coordinating fabric, one for each potholder. Fold in half, right sides together, and sew. Turn right side out and press. Then pin a loop to the right side of the potholder front, aligning the raw edge with the top center of the potholder. Stitch or baste in place.

13 For each potholder, layer the following from bottom to top in this order: insulated batting, backing fabric (right side up), and potholder front (right side down). Pin carefully along previously sewn line, and be sure to catch all layers and leave a 2-inch (5.1 cm) opening at the bottom of the potholder. Stitch. Then turn potholders right side out and press. Stitch opening closed by hand.

figure 1

child's play

$\mathcal{B}$ring your little artist's sketches to life by transforming them into an embroidered keepsake. Coordinating scraps of patterned fabric and perky rickrack make for a portable gallery you'll want to display in any room in the house.

DESIGNER
CASSI GRIFFIN

WHAT YOU NEED

Basic sewing tools

3 coordinating scraps of print cotton for fabrics A, B, and C, none less than 4 x 6 inches (10.2 x 15.2 cm)

9 x 18-inch (22.9 x 45.7 cm) piece of print cotton for fabric D

5 x 5-inch (12.7 x 12.7 cm) square of linen for embroidery

Child's drawing to embroider

Water-soluble fabric marker

Embroidery hoop

Embroidery floss

Embroidery needle

1 yard (.9 m) of 1-inch (2.5 cm) rickrack

Polyester fiberfill

SEAM ALLOWANCE

½ inch (1.3 cm) unless otherwise noted

FINISHED SIZE

12 x 4 inches (30.5 x 10.2 cm)

WHAT YOU DO

1 For the front of the pillow, cut 3½ x 5-inch (8.9 x 12.7 cm) rectangles each from fabrics A and D. Take care to cut from the end of fabric D as you will be using the rest of fabric D to create the back of the pillow. Then cut 2½ x 5-inch (6.4 x 12.7 cm) rectangles each from fabrics B and C. Cut another rectangle from fabric D for the back of the pillow that is 5 x 13 inches (12.7 x 33 cm).

2 Transfer the child's drawing to the linen square using the water-soluble fabric marker. Place the fabric in the hoop and embroider using floss colors that coordinate with the fabric prints. Use simple stitches, such as the backstitch, chain stitch, and running stitch. When done, remove the fabric from hoop and press, but do not iron over the embroidery.

3 Piece the cotton prints. Stitch A to B. Then stitch C to the 3½ x 5-inch (8.9 x 12.7 cm) rectangle of fabric D.

4 With right sides together, pin the patch made of fabrics A and B to one side of the embroidered linen square, and pin the patch made from fabrics C and D to the other side (figure 1). Stitch, then press all seams open.

5 Lay the large rectangle cut from fabric D right side up. Center the rickrack along the front seam allowance (figure 2), pin and baste the rickrack. Pin the pillow front to the back with right sides together. Sew both long ends and one of the short sides.

6 On the open short side, press the seam allowance under at the opening. Trim the corners, then turn pillow right side out. Poke the corners out as needed and press.

7 Stuff with the polyester fiberfill. Do not overstuff. Stitch the opening closed using the slipstitch.

figure 1

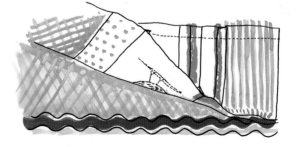

figure 2

93

give

sew convenient 95
sew pretty ornaments 98
at your fingertips 100
timeless treasures 102
recipe for happiness 105
hold anything 108
a bird for all seasons 110
passport, please 112
patchwork doorstop 116

wedding memories 119
i ❤ you coasters 122
keep your place 124
sweet tooth 127
hearts on a string 130
undercover portfolio 132
wake, rattle & stroll 136
"i do" 138

sew convenient

*I*f you have a friend who brings sewing projects with her wherever she goes—on vacation, in the car, or at the soccer game—she will adore this little gift. It will get her up and sewing in no time!

DESIGNER

KATHERINE ACCETTURA

95

WHAT YOU NEED

Basic sewing tools

Patterns (page 294)

Fabric for the inner shell,
10 x 10 inches (25.4 x 25.4 cm)

Fabric for the outer shell,
10 x 10 inches (25.4 x 25.4 cm)

Cotton batting or fleece for
padding, 10 x 10 inches
(25.4 x 25.4 cm)

Coordinating wool or acrylic felt,
7 x 7 inches (17.8 x 17.8 cm)

Hook-and-loop tape, about 1 inch
(2.5 cm) long

Coordinating shank button, small
to medium in size

WHAT YOU DO

1 Using the large pattern, cut one shape each from the inner fabric, the outer fabric, and the batting or fleece. Using the small pattern, cut one shape from the felt.

2 Layer the large pieces from bottom to top: the batting/fleece, the inner fabric (right side up), and the outer fabric (right side down). Pin the layers together on all sides.

3 Using a small stitch, sew ¼ inch (6 mm) from the edge all the way around, leaving a 1-inch (2.5 cm) gap to turn the layers right side out. Stop after sewing each arch and pivot the needle while raising the presser foot (see page 20 for more machine-sewing instructions). Emphasize the curves during this step if possible.

4 Trim the edges to reduce the seam allowance. Clip tiny notches into the edges so the shape will remain flat and round when turned right side out.

5 Flip the fabric right side out through the gap. Press it flat with the iron. Hand sew the gap closed and then topstitch close to the edge all the way around.

6 Pin the felt piece to the center of the inner fabric, aligning the contours of the arches. Use at least four pins. Sew through all layers from the dip between each arch into the center (refer to the pattern on page 294).

7 Cut the hook-and-loop tape so it fits on the tab's underside. Make sure you can't see it from the top of the tab. Pin it in place and sew closely around the edges.

8 Fold up the fabric piece by bunching the arches together so they touch, collapsing on the center (figure 1). Line up the arches as much as possible. Fold down the tab to see where to affix the other side of the hook-and-loop tape. Mark the spot on the outer fabric and sew it down.

9 Affix the shank button to the top of the tab. Now wherever you (or your friends) go, you can safely travel with sewing needles.

figure 1

NEEDLING PERSONALITY

You may choose to do some decorative stitching as well. Give this gift your own personal touch; your friends will notice.

sew pretty ornaments

Make these exquisite little ornaments for friends and family, or stitch up a bunch for your own seasonal decor. Unlike glass ornaments, these hand-sewn beauties won't break, so you can enjoy them year after year.

DESIGNER

JOAN K. MORRIS

WHAT YOU NEED

Basic sewing tools

Scrap paper

6 assorted similar fabrics

Matching thread

8 x 8-inch (20.3 x 20.3 cm) piece of felt

8 inches (20.3 cm) of gold cord

Knitting needle

15 inches (38.1 cm) matching trim or ribbon

Hot glue gun

SEAM ALLOWANCE

1/4 inch (0.6 cm)

WHAT YOU DO

1 Draw out your ornament design on the scrap paper, and cut it out. Draw a rectangle 1 1/4 x 4 inches (3.2 x 10.2 cm), and cut it out.

2 Using the rectangle pattern, cut out three rectangles from each of the six fabrics. Choose two fabrics, and cut two 2 x 4-inch (5.1 x 10.2 cm) rectangles from each.

3 Lay out the fabrics in the pattern of the ornaments: six small rectangles vertically, two small rectangles horizontally under that, a large rectangle on top, and a large one at the bottom (figure 1). You will have two sets.

figure 1

4 Machine stitch the vertical pieces together with a 1/4-inch (0.6 cm) seam allowance. Press the seams open. Machine stitch the horizontal pieces to the bottom. Press seam open. Stitch one of the large rectangles to the bottom and one to the top, and center them on the piece. Repeat this for the second set.

5 Place the felt on the wrong side of one of the pieces. Place its matching piece right sides together with the first. Trim a little of the felt off. Cut a 6-inch (15.2 cm) piece of the gold cord, and fold it in half. Place the cord between the two pieces, with the cut end up.

6 Place the ornament pattern in position on top of the piece, and pin in place. Machine stitch around the outside of the pattern. Leave open a small section at the bottom to allow turning right side out. Clip curves, and turn right side out. Push out corners with the knitting needle. Press flat, folding the opening inside. Hand stitch the opening closed. Use the hot glue gun to hold the trim in place.

atyourfingertips

$\mathcal{P}$ ins couldn't be closer when you need them than on this fabulous finger pincushion. It's a great gift for a crafter or sewer, too.

DESIGNER

JULIE ROMINE

WHAT YOU NEED

Basic sewing tools

Lightweight cardboard

Scraps of coordinating cotton fabric

Sewing machine (optional)

Ribbon, rickrack, or buttons

WHAT YOU DO

1 Make a pattern from the template (page 296) onto lightweight cardboard.

2 Lay the fabrics with right sides together, and trace lightly around the triangle with a pencil.

3 Sew before cutting the fabric, stitching directly on the line drawn. Make sure to backstitch at the start and finish, and leave a gap on the longest edge for turning the pincushion to the right side.

4 Cut around the sewn triangle, leaving a ¼-inch seam allowance. Clip the corners, and turn right side out.

5 Stuff the side points lightly, using the eraser end of the pencil to help push the stuffing in. Stuff the main body firmly. Whipstitch the opening closed.

6 Overlap the outside points of the triangle, and hand stitch them together with a double-threaded needle for strength. Then stitch the center of a small length of ribbon onto the inside of the sewn points. Wrap the ribbon around, fold under the end, and stitch in place.

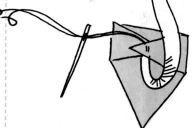

7 Be creative with rickrack, ribbons, and buttons to embellish your finger pincushion.

timelesstreasures

With your careful hand embroidery, these pincushions will be heirlooms to pass down to the next generation of crafters and sewers.

DESIGNER

JEN SEGREST

ROUNDING CORNERS

If you cut right-handed, round the right side of the corners for a clover leaf or flower first. Then flip the felt over and repeat on the other side. Try the opposite if you're left-handed.

WHAT YOU NEED

Basic sewing tools

Craft felt, various bright colors

Craft thread, matching colors

2 felt buttons (page 104)

WHAT YOU DO

1 Cut two 3-inch circles from felt for the top and bottom of the pincushion. Cut a 2-inch-wide strip of felt long enough to go around the circle with a little overlap—about 9½ inches—for the side.

2 Hand sew the side to the top circle using a buttonhole stitch, overlapping the ends of the side toward the finish. Cut any excess length from the side.

3 Repeat step 2 to sew the side to the bottom, but stop three-quarters of the way around to begin stuffing.

4 Stuff very firmly with polyester fiberfill, being sure to stuff into the edges and corners. Then continue sewing to close the gap. Add more stuffing as you go, making the cushion as firm as possible.

5 Mark the center of the top and bottom of the cushion. Make a felt button (see sidebar, page 104), and thread a long needle with the thread hanging from the finished button. Push the needle into the top center mark and out the bottom center mark. Leave the thread hanging.

6 Repeat with a second button, starting from the bottom center and bringing the needle out on the top center, so a button is on each side and its thread is on the opposite side.

7 Insert the threaded needle back into the top center, under the button, and bring it out on the bottom center, under the other button. Pull both threads taut to tuft, or dimple, the pincushion on the top and bottom. Make a surgeon's knot to tie it off. Trim the thread.

Felt Button

Create two of these hand-worked buttons to use for the Timeless Treasure pincushion. You will need felt and a needle and thread in a matching color.

1 Cut a 1½- to 2-inch circle of felt. Thread a needle with a matching color of thread, knotting it.

2 Sew a running stitch around the outside edge of the circle for a drawstring. Draw the thread tightly shut, knot it, and then flatten the ball.

3 Run the threaded needle through the gathered center and out the folded edge, and sew another running stitch on the folded edge itself.

4 Draw tightly for a drawstring again, and press the gather into the middle as you pull the thread to close around it. Pull tight and run the thread to the opposite side. Pull again, and knot. Repeat several times to close up any gap. Leave the thread hanging to use to attach the button later.

9 At the end of each branch, make a three-spoke wheel of chain stitches in another color, and then whipstitch twice over the twig for a more finished look. Or, use a single chain stitch for a flower bud. Stitch felt flowers to the top and sides as well, if desired.

10 Fill in open areas with running vertical and horizontal stitches, beads, or flowers made with a chain stitch.

8 Embroider a branch around the side using a feather stitch. If desired, cut felt for decorations, and slide them onto the needle, knotting them into the embroidery as you go.

CIRCLES FROM SQUARES

To improvise a 3-inch circle, cut a 3-inch square first. Then, just round the corners into a circle.

recipe for happiness

*T*his little house has it all: one part yummy, two parts sweet, and a dollop of finger-licking fun. Use a treasured recipe that's been passed down through the years to create your own special keepsake.

DESIGNER

BETHANY MANN

WHAT YOU NEED

Basic sewing tools

8 x 10-inch (20.3 x 25.4 cm) washable, inkjet-ready, printable cotton sheet

2 fabric scraps in two main colors, 12 x 12 inches (30.5 x 30.5 cm)

2 accent pieces of fabric, 8 x 8 inches (20.3 x 20.3 cm)

Computer

Scanner

Inkjet printer

Rotary cutter

White thread

2 pieces of 10 x 10-inch (25.4 x 25.4 cm) batting

4 inches (10.2 cm) of bias tape

Large button

Thread in black or contrasting color to main fabric for hand quilting

Quilting needle

SEAM ALLOWANCE

¼ inch (0.6 cm)

105

WHAT YOU DO

1 Choose a recipe card and a photo of someone enjoying the recipe. With the computer and scanner, scan and resize the recipe card to be about 2½ x 4¼ inches (6.4 x 10.8 cm) and the photo to be 2¾ x 4¼ inches (7 x 10.8 cm). Print the card and photo on the cotton sheet.

2 Follow the instructions on the package to set the ink.

3 Trim the photo and recipe card with a ¼-inch (0.6 cm) border on all sides. With the rotary cutter and ruler, cut out the strips 1¼ inches (3.2 cm) wide for the front of the house. In a contrasting fabric color, cut out strips 1 inch (2.5 cm) wide for the roof. Then cut the striped window patch to be 2¼ x 3 inches (5.7 x 7.6 cm), and cut out the floral door panel to be 4¾ x 4 inches (12 x 10.2 cm).

4 Sew the window to a 3-inch (7.6 cm) strip of the house fabric, and then sew on the recipe card, end to end. Next, sew the photo to a 4¾-inch-long (12 cm) strip of house fabric, and seam the door's floral panel patch to the photo and strip of fabric. Press open all the seams. You should have two strips of patches.

5 Sew the panel with the recipe card to the top of a 7¼-inch (18.4 cm) length of the house fabric strips you cut out earlier. Then sew the photo panel to the bottom, and press open the seams.

6 Cut out a triangle of fabric 6 x 6 x 7¼ inches (15.2 x 15.2 x 18.4 cm). Sew a 1-inch-wide (2.5 cm) roof strip to the right 6-inch (15.2 cm) side of the triangle. Sew the other roof strip to the left 6-inch (15.2) side of the triangle, and make sure to overlap the other roof strip as well. Sew the roof to the top of the finished patchwork house.

7 Use the house as a template to cut a back panel and two pieces of batting trimmed a ¼ inch (0.6 cm) smaller than the house. Pin together right sides

OUTER SPACE

Printable cotton sheets are available at many quilting and craft stores. You can use the extra cotton to print pictures for other projects, but be sure to leave unused ½-inch (1.3 cm) portions between photos for the seam allowance.

facing with a short piece of bias tape across the peak of the roof, with the tape sandwiched between the layers to act as a hanging loop on the back.

8 Seam the patchwork to the backing, and leave a 5-inch (12.7 cm) opening on the bottom. Trim the corners, and turn it inside out. Insert the batting into the opening at the bottom.

9 From the roof fabric, cut out the 2 x 3-inch (5.1 x 7.6 cm) door. Press under all sides, and pin

in place on the flowered patch. Using a hidden stitch, close up the opening at the bottom, tucking in the door bottom. With a doubled black thread, do freehand quilting. Stitch the button in the roof area.

IN THE SPOTLIGHT

You may choose to hand appliqué the door into place then stitch to highlight the house and aspects of the photo. For freehand stitches, try using tailor's chalk and a ruler to mark lines to follow.

hold anything

DESIGNER

CELINE REID

$\mathcal{P}$art of the fun of receiving these stylish containers is counting all the rooms in the house where they could come in handy. As a bonus, you can fill them with additional gifts before you wrap them up!

WHAT YOU NEED

Basic sewing tools

⅓ yard (30.5 cm) of medium-weight fabric (e.g., upholstery fabric or heavy linen)

⅓ yard (30.5 cm) of printed cotton fabric

SEAM ALLOWANCE

⅜ inch (1 cm)

WHAT YOU DO

1 Cut two 10½ x 9-inch (26.7 x 22.9 cm) rectangles in the medium-weight fabric. Cut a circle with a 6¾-inch (17.1 cm) diameter. These pieces make the outer fabric of the box. Repeat with the printed cotton to fashion the inner fabric.

2 Pin the outer fabric rectangles together, right sides facing, and straight-stitch along each short side. Repeat with the inner fabric, except sew only one short side completely. On the other short side, sew about 3 inches (7.6 cm), leave a 4-inch (10.2 cm) gap, and then sew to the end.

3 Pin the outer fabric circle to a short side of the outer fabric rectangles, right sides together, and sew all around. Repeat with the inner fabric, using the fully sewn short side as the base.

4 Insert the inner box into the outer box, right sides together. Sew the two boxes together at the top edge.

5 Turn the box right side out through the opening. Close the opening with a straight stitch.

6 Shape the box by stuffing the inner fabric inside the outer fabric. To finish, topstitch along the top edge. Turn the top of the box out, and it's ready to use.

BOTH SIDES NOW

If you make this project with heavy-duty fabrics—ones that will stand up to heavy use—the box is completely reversible. Make a few and turn one inside out to make a decorative statement.

a bird for all seasons

*T*his present gives you a two-fer: The fabric-wrapped hanger
will delight, but the dangling sachet bird will surprise. She'll
keep clothes smelling fresh on and off the hanger.

DESIGNER

FIONA HESFORD

WHAT YOU NEED

Basic sewing tools

Patterns (page 296)

Padded clothes hanger, about 17 inches (43.2 cm) wide

2 pieces of knitted striped fabric, 6 x 6 inches (15.2 x 15.2 cm) and 5 x 17 inches (12.7 x 43.2 cm)

2 pieces of ribbon, one lilac and one blue-and-white gingham, each 12 inches (30.5 cm) long

Craft glue

Square of fusible and dissolvable stabilizer, 6 inches (15.2 cm) to a side

2 squares of felt in white and lilac, about 4 inches (10.2 cm) to a side

Small scraps of brown and orange felt

1 ounce of dried lavender

2 buttons, ⅜ inch (1 cm)

Black sewing thread

Plastic kitchen funnel (optional)

SEAM ALLOWANCE

¼ inch (6 mm), unless otherwise noted

WHAT YOU DO

MAKING THE HANGER

1 Unscrew the metal hook from the hanger and set it aside.

2 Fold the larger piece of knitted fabric in half lengthwise with right sides together. Sew around the edges, leaving one narrow end open. Round off the edges by sewing across the corners.

3 Turn it inside out. Push the hanger into the knitted tube and sew up the open end by hand.

4 Replace the metal hook. Tie a tight lilac ribbon bow around the hook. Fix it in place with a blob of glue.

MAKING THE BIRD

5 Iron on the fusible stabilizer to the wrong side of the knitted fabric square. Using Template A, copy one bird shape on the wrong side of the knit and one on the wrong side of the white felt. Cut them out.

6 Using Template B, copy two wing shapes on the lilac felt. Copy two feather shapes using Template C on the brown felt and the lilac felt. Copy a beak shape onto the orange felt using Template D. Cut out all the shapes.

7 Pin and sew the wings to the right side of both bird shapes. Turn the knit bird shape right side down, and pin the beak in place, sticking out past the front of the bird head (see the project photograph). Pin the ends of the ribbon to the middle of the bird's back.

8 Leaving a 2-inch (5.1 cm) opening at the base, baste together the two bird shapes, right sides facing. Sew around the edges. Trim the seams and nick the curved edges.

9 Turn it right side out and fill the bird with the lavender. Sew up the opening by hand. Attach the button eyes with black thread and add the felt feathers at the tail.

passport, please

DESIGNER

LISA COX

This is the gift your travel-loving friends never knew they needed until they unwrapped it. It's small enough to fit inside a jacket pocket, but large enough to contain all their important papers.

WHAT YOU NEED

Basic sewing tools

¼ yard (22.9 cm) or one fat quarter each of quilting cotton in two prints (B and C)

Sheet of thin clear plastic (often sold as clear tablecloth plastic)

Medium-weight fusible interfacing

Striped linen (Pattern A), 10½-inch (26.7 cm) square

Solid-colored linen, 4½ x 3¼ inches (11.4 x 8.3 cm)

Thread to match your fabrics

Bias tape maker (optional)

8-inch (20.3 cm) beige zipper

Silver key ring hoop

WHAT YOU DO

1 From the Pattern B quilting cotton, cut out two pieces: one 10½-inch (26.7 cm) square and one 9½ x 10½-inch (24.1 x 26.7 cm) rectangle.

2 From the Pattern C quilting cotton, cut out 13 pieces: five at 1½ x 10½ inches (3.8 x 26.7 cm), one at 1¾ x 2 inches (4.4 x 5.1 cm), two at 2 x 2 inches (5.1 x 5.1 cm), three at 2½ x 22 inches (6.4 x 55.9 cm), one at ½ x 5 inches (1.3 x 12.7 cm), and a last one at 2 x 3 inches (5.1 x 7.6 cm).

3 From the plastic sheet, cut out three pieces: one 4 x 10½ inches (10.2 x 26.7 cm), one 4¾ x 4½ inches (12 x 11.4 cm), and one 4¾ x 5 inches (12 x 12.7 cm).

4 From the interfacing, cut out four pieces: two 10½-inch (26.7 cm) squares, one 9½ x 10½-inch (24.1 x 26.7 cm) rectangle, and one 4½ x 3¼- inch (11.4 x 8.3 cm) rectangle. Iron the interfacing onto the wrong sides of the Pattern A piece, both Pattern B pieces, and the solid linen piece.

5 Press ¼ inch (6 mm) under on all sides of the solid linen. Turn under one short end another ¼ inch (6 mm) and stitch across. Fold the Pattern A fabric in half. With the fold to the left, position the solid linen 1½ inches (3.8 cm) from the bottom and ½ inch (1.3 cm) from the fold. Stitch it down on three sides as shown in the project photo.

PATTERN COMPLEMENTS

While you may choose any complementary fabrics to create your gift, the designer used a brown/cream linen print (Pattern A), a brown polka dot cotton (Pattern B), and a brown/black floral cotton (Pattern C). Whichever patterns you choose, make sure they all work nicely together.

6 With the 1¾ x 2-inch (4.4 x 5.1 cm) Pattern C piece, form bias tape ⅜ inch (1 cm) wide. Stitch the long open edge closed. Baste the two raw edges together to create a loop. Use the five 1½ x 10½-inch (3.8 x 26.7 cm) Pattern C strips to make more ⅜-inch (1 cm) bias tape, but do not stitch them closed.

7 Center the 2 x 2-inch (5.1 x 5.1 cm) Pattern C pieces over each end of the zipper (near the metal stoppers) with the right side up. Stitch both in place. Fold the fabric over to the back of the zipper tape (figure 1).

8 Wrap a bias strip around the long edge of the large plastic sheet and pin it down. Stitch it ⅛ inch (3 mm) from the inside edge. Pin that edge to one side of the zipper and, using a zipper foot, stitch it ⅛ inch (3 mm) from the edge. Attach a bias strip to the other side of the zipper. Baste the raw edges of the plastic to the left side of the 10½-inch (26.7 cm) Pattern B square, right sides up. Stitch down the zippered side ⅛ inch (3 mm) from the edge, catching the step 6 loop 2½ inches (6.4 cm) from the top.

9 Form a narrow strip of bias tape with the ½ x 5-inch Pattern C piece. Poke it through the end of the zipper and tie a lark's head knot for a zipper pull.

10 Form the 2 x 3-inch (5.1 x 7.6 cm) Pattern C fabric into a bias strip. Stitch the open side closed. Create a loop around the key ring and baste the raw ends along the top edge in the middle of the plastic zippered pocket.

11 Fold the smaller Pattern B fabric in half, wrong sides facing, so it measures 4¾ x 10½ inches (12 x 26.7 cm). Wrap the top short edge of both remaining plastic sheets with a ⅜-inch (1 cm) bias strip. Stitch along both long edges of the bias strip, trimming to fit. Baste the bottom edge of the larger plastic sheet to the bottom edge of the Pattern B fabric with the fold to the left. Wrap a bias strip around the bottom edge of the other plastic sheet and place it on the Pattern B fabric above the other plastic piece. The bound edges of the plastic pieces should align. Fold the bottom piece out of the way and stitch it down along both edges of the bias tape. Stitch a 10½-inch bias strip over the folded edge of the Pattern B fabric with two rows, catching the raw edges of both plastic pockets as you sew (figure 2).

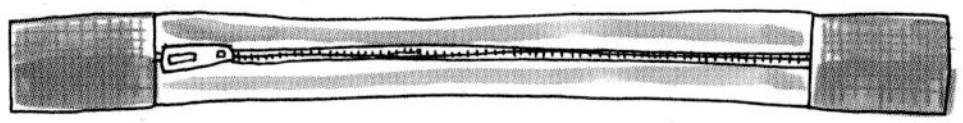

figure 1

figure 2

12 Position the step 11 pouch on the right side of the larger Pattern B fabric and baste it in place along the top, side, and bottom. Layer the whole thing on the Pattern A piece, wrong sides together, and baste them around the perimeter. Join the remaining bias strips and sew them around the outside edges, mitering the corners. Hand sew the inside edge to complete. Do not press the finished wallet.

145

patchwork doorstop

DESIGNER

ELIZABETH HARTMAN

$\mathcal{F}$or the friend who has everything else: a quilted doorstop. Once you create its nine-block design, it might even be too pretty to hide on the floor.

WHAT YOU NEED

Basic sewing tools

Scraps of wool suiting: 2 strips, each 5½ x 3¼ inches (14 x 8.3 cm); 2 strips, each 10 x 3¼ inches (25.4 x 8.3 cm); and 1 strip, 2½ x 9 inches (6.4 x 22.9 cm)

Strip of lightweight fusible interfacing, 2½ x 9 inches (6.4 x 22.9 cm)

Scraps of printed cotton: one 10-inch (25.4 cm) square; one strip, 2½ x 9 inches (6.4 x 22.9 cm); and nine 2½-inch (6.4 cm) squares

Two 10-inch (25.4 cm) squares of fusible fleece

Zipper, 7 inches (17.8 cm) in length

Decorative plastic button

4–5 pounds of dried beans

SEAM ALLOWANCE

½ inch (1.3 cm)

WHAT YOU DO

1 Fuse the interfacing to the matching strip of wool suiting. Fold and press the long sides of the strip into the center, wrong sides together. Repeat with the 2½ x 9-inch (6.4 x 22.9 cm) scrap of cotton. Layer the two strips, wrong sides together, and stitch close to both long edges. Set the handle aside.

2 Iron one square of fusible fleece to the wrong side of the 10-inch (25.4 cm) cotton square. Machine-quilt in any pattern you want. Then pick one edge as the bottom and press it under ½ inch (1.3 cm), wrong sides together.

3 Arrange the nine 2½-inch (6.4 cm) cotton squares on a work surface. Stitch the squares together into three rows of three. Press the seams open and pin the rows together, lining up the seams, and then stitch the three rows into a nine-patch block. Press the seams open again.

4 Sew the 5½ x 3¼-inch (14 x 8.3 cm) wool suiting strips to the top and bottom of the patch block. Press the seams open. Then sew the 10 x 3¼-inch (25.4 x 8.3 cm) wool suiting strips to the left and right sides of the block. Again, press the seams open. Trim any uneven edges so the block is 10 inches (25.4 cm) square.

5 Iron the last square of fusible fleece to the wrong side of the block. Machine-quilt as desired. Press the bottom edge under ½ inch (1.3 cm), wrong sides together.

6 Pin the zipper to the center of the folded bottom edge of the front panel. Using a zipper foot, slowly stitch the zipper to the panel, removing pins as you go. Pin the other side of the zipper to the folded bottom edge of the back panel and sew it in place

the same way. Open the zipper about 7 inches (17.8 cm) and keep it open for now.

7 With right sides together, pin the front and back panels along the top edge. Sew the two panels together. Press open the seam. Pin and sew the side seams, clipping the corners and pressing open the seams.

8 Measure and mark a ½-inch (1.3 cm) square at each corner. Trim the corners along these lines.

9 Starting at the bottom corner with the zipper's metal base (not the pull), open up the corner and stack the right side of the bottom seam on the right side of the side seam. Pin and stitch them together. If you've centered the zipper, the seam falls just outside the zipper base. Repeat at the opposite bottom corner.

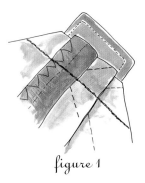

figure 1

10 Thread the whole handle through the top corner openings with the printed side facing the right side. Press one corner as you did the bottom corners, but keep the handle end threaded through. Stitch the corner closed, catching the handle (figure 1).

11 Repeat with the other top corner, making sure the handle isn't pulled too tight or left too loose. Trim the handle ends so they are even with the corner seams. Reinforce all four corner seams with several rows of zigzag stitching.

12 Turn the doorstop right side out. Sew the button on the center square of the patch block. Then fill the doorstop with the dried beans.

QUILT MARKS

You can use any quilt pattern you like, but the designer sewed a 1¼-inch (3.2 cm) diamond pattern. She measured it out with a quilting ruler and used a disappearing ink marker on the fabric as a guide (although masking tape also works well).

wedding memories

*J*ournals to give to bridesmaids, a register for guests to sign, a scrapbook for a honeymoon vacation—a bride-to-be can find so many uses for these classy little albums.

DESIGNER

TERRY TAYLOR

WHAT YOU NEED

Basic sewing tools

Hot pressed or cold pressed watercolor paper

Bone folder or table knife

Phone book

Awl

2 or 3 coordinating fabrics

Waxed linen or heavy thread

2 sharp needles with large eyes

1-inch buttons

WHAT YOU DO

1 Using the ruler, score and tear the watercolor paper into 5½ x 14-inch (14 x 35.6 cm) pieces. You need nine for an 18-page book or 12 for a 24-page book. Stack three or four pieces together, and then fold the stack in half to create a signature that's 5½ x 7 inches (14 x 17.8 cm). Use the bone folder to crease the fold. Make three signatures for each book.

2 Cut a piece of scrap paper into a 5½ x 6-inch (14 x 15.2 cm) rectangle. Fold it in half so it's 5½ x 3 inches (14 x 7.6 cm). Unfold the paper and mark the center point (2¾ inches [7 cm] from the edge) in the crease. Then mark ¼ inch (6 mm) from both edges in the crease. Finally, mark 1¼ inches (3.2 cm) from both edges in the crease.

3 Open the phone book and lay one open signature in the book. Place the scrap paper on top. Use the awl to pierce holes through the signature at the marks. Repeat for each signature. Set the pages aside.

4 Sandwich three layers of fabric, with the top and bottom right sides out. Pin them together.

With the pinking shears, cut a 6⅜ x 15¼-inch (16.2 x 38.7 cm) rectangle. Vary each book by using a different fabric on the bottom layer of the stack.

5 Machine-stitch across the width or the length, through all layers, with evenly spaced lines of stitching. Optionally, you may add a second layer of curved lines with a different-colored thread. This is the book cover.

6 Embellish the cover any way you want. For example, stitch strips of coordinating fabric to the cover to create a decorative spine (as shown in the project photo). You can also embroider the cover, sew on appliqués or simple geometric shapes, or any number of other embellishments. The sky's the limit!

7 Create a tie for the book with a 1⅛ x 8-inch (2.8 x 20.3 cm) strip of fabric. Fold it in thirds lengthwise and stitch it together with a zigzag or straight stitch. Then machine-stitch the tie to the back cover of the book.

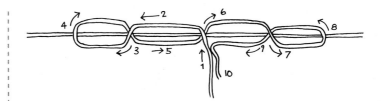

figure 1

8 Fold the book cover in half and iron the folded crease. Slip one signature of watercolor paper into the ironed crease. Cut three 18-inch (45.7 cm) lengths of the waxed linen or heavy thread. Thread a length onto one of the large-eyed needles.

9 Poke the needle through the center hole of the signature, from the inside. Pull the needle through the paper and the cover, leaving a 3-inch (7.6 cm) tail. Back inside the book, poke the second needle without thread into an adjacent hole. Push the tip of the needle through the paper and the cover. Use that tip to show where to stitch the threaded needle back in the cover and through the pages (figure 1).

10 Stitch out through the next adjacent hole and then back down through the previous hole. At the center,

stitch up through the hole to the outside. Back inside, poke the unthreaded needle into the adjacent hole on the other side (the side you haven't yet sewn). Pass the threaded needle through the cover and pages at that point. Poke the thread out through the last unstitched hole and back in through the previous hole. Tie the two thread ends together in a small, tight knot.

11 Place another signature page on one side of the stitched stack. Repeat steps 9 and 10 to attach the new signature in place, about ⅛ to ¼ inch (3 to 6 mm) from the first. Repeat with the last signature on the opposite side of the first.

12 Stitch a decorative button in place on the front cover. Wind the tie around the button to seal in the memories.

i ♥ you coasters

DESIGNER

WENDY ARACICH

You can whip up these adorable coasters in a jiffy if you need a last-minute gift. Use fabric remnants you have on hand to tailor the coasters to your friend's style or décor.

WHAT YOU NEED

Basic sewing tools

Pink felt, ¼ yard (22.9 cm)

Black-and-white polka dot fabric remnant

Black embroidery floss

Embroidery needle

Pink thread

WHAT YOU DO

1 Cut eight 5-inch (12.7 cm) squares of pink felt and four 4½-inch (11.4 cm) squares from the fabric.

2 On scrap paper, sketch a heart that's no wider than 4½ inches (11.4 cm) and no taller than 3 inches (7.6 cm). Cut out the heart template.

3 Center the template on a felt square and trace the heart. Remove the template and carefully cut out the heart shape. Repeat for the other felt squares.

4 Pin the fabric squares, right side up, underneath the cut felt so it shows through the heart shape. With the embroidery floss, sew a running stitch around the perimeter of the shapes, ¼ inch (6 mm) from the edge. Turn the coaster over and trim the fabric about ½ inch (1.3 cm) outside the stitches.

5 Pin the coaster back to the front, wrong sides together. Using the pink thread, machine stitch around the perimeter, leaving a ½-inch (1.3 cm) seam allowance. Trim the seams to ¼ inch (6 mm). Repeat with the remaining coasters.

A PENNY (MORE) FOR YOUR THOUGHTS

Although you can use synthetic wool for these coasters, wool felt works best. Spend a little more, and make a gift you'll be proud to give.

keep your place

Stitched-in magnets hold this bookmark on its page, but it's your choice of colors and patterns that really does the attracting. Someone in your book group has a birthday coming up? Another present problem is solved.

DESIGNER

JOAN K. MORRIS

WHAT YOU NEED

Basic sewing tools

6 pieces of ½-inch (1.3 cm) wide self-adhesive tape magnet, each 1¼ inch in length

2 pieces of stiff quilt interfacing, each 1¾ x 2⅞ inches (4.4 x 7.3 cm)

Strip of cotton fabric (for the center), 2 x 6 inches (5.1 x 15.2 cm)

2 pieces of cotton fabric (for the background), each 3 x 7 inches (7.6 x 17.8 cm)

Button

WHAT YOU DO

1 Remove the tape backing from one piece of magnet tape and place it ⅜ inch (1 cm) from the short end on a piece of the stiff quilt interfacing. Line up two more magnets below the first, one right next to the other. Repeat on the other piece of quilt interfacing (figure 1).

figure 1

2 Press all the edges of the center fabric piece ½ inch (1.3 cm). Center it on top of one of the background fabric pieces, right sides up, and pin it in place. Machine-stitch all the way around as close as you can to the edge.

3 Place the second background fabric piece on top of the sewn piece, right sides together. Machine-stitch all the way around, ¼ inch (6 mm) in from the edge, leaving a 2-inch (5.1 cm) opening on one of the long sides. Clip the corners.

4 Turn the piece right side out and push out the corners. Press the piece flat, folding under the raw seams. Slide one piece of interfacing through the opening with the magnets facing the back. Push it toward one end of the bookmark. Repeat with the other piece of interfacing, again with the magnets facing the back, but push it toward the other end of the bookmark.

5 Topstitch all the way around, as close as you can get to the edge, catching both sides of the opening. Find the center of the bookmark and topstitch across it. Topstitch ¼ inch (6 mm) in from the first topstitch line, all the way around. Be careful not to catch the magnets. Topstitch across the bookmark ¾ inch (1.9 cm) on either side of the center stitch. Hand stitch the button in place at the very center of the bookmark, where it will fold over.

MAGNETIC ADVICE

When you're sewing with the magnets in the piece, remember that they will be attracted to the metal plate of the sewing machine under the foot. The fabric might stick occasionally while you're sewing, so proceed slowly to get it right.

sweet tooth

𝒲ho among us doesn't recall the anticipation of a nighttime visit from the Tooth Fairy? Carry on an honored tradition with this candy-colored pocket pillow, ready to hang from the door.

DESIGNER

NATHALIE MORNU

WHAT YOU NEED

Basic sewing tools

¼ yard (22.8 cm) of fabric for the pocket

¼ yard (22.8 cm) of fabric for the body of the pillow

Water-soluble marker

Embroidery hoop

Embroidery floss

Embroidery needle

1 yard (.9 m) of ribbon, ³⁄₁₆ inch (5 mm) wide

Polyester fiberfill

SEAM ALLOWANCE

½ inch (1.3 cm) unless otherwise noted

FINISHED SIZE

9½ x 5½ inches (24.1 x 14 cm)

WHAT YOU DO

1 Enlarge the templates on page 297 and cut them out.

2 Trace the outline of the pocket template onto the appropriate fabric but **don't** cut it out. Transfer the embroidery design onto the fabric, and write your child's name nearby with the soluble marker, making sure to stay within ½ inch (1.3 cm) of the inside of the outline to accommodate the seam allowance.

3 Using the embroidery hoop to hold the fabric, embroider the designs using the floss and the embroidery needle. Use the outline or stem stitch for the design and name, and make French knots for the eyes.

4 Cut the pocket. Fold it with wrong sides together at the fold line and press. Cut a piece of ribbon 7¼ inches (18.4 cm) long. On the embroidered half of the pocket, pin the ribbon close to the edge of the fold (figure 1), and stitch it down. Trim away the excess ribbon at either end.

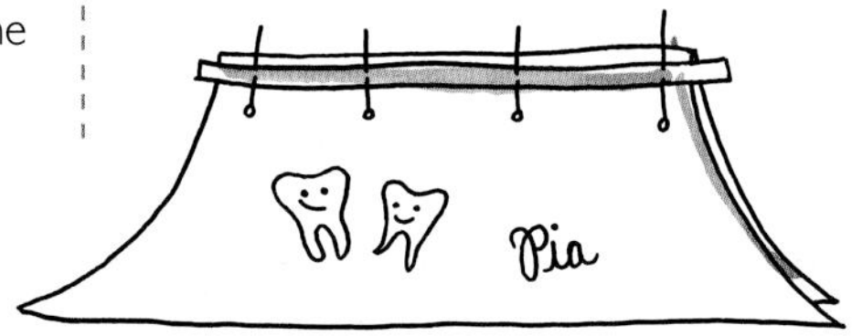

figure 1

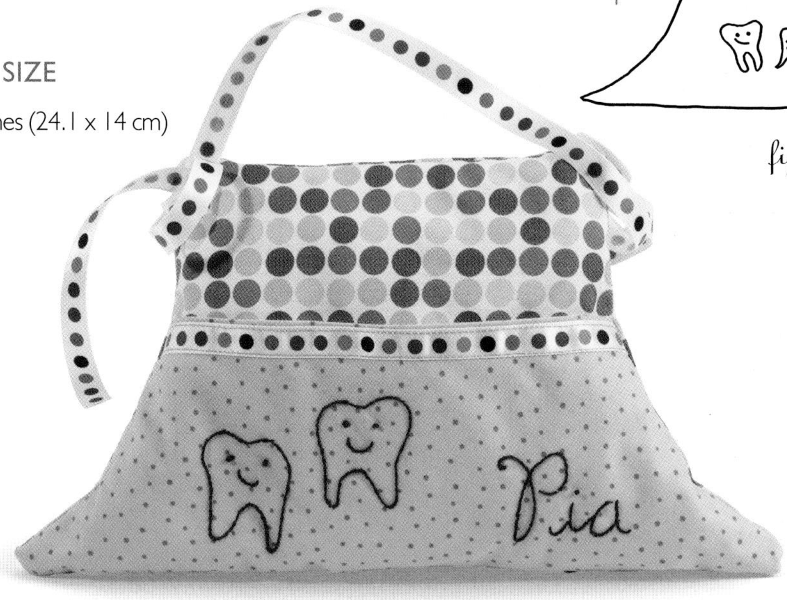

128

5 Cut the pieces for the body of the pillow out of the fabric. Place one right side up on your work surface. Lay the pocket with embroidered side up over it, matching raw edges. Over these, lay the second body piece, right side down with raw edges aligned. Pin, and then stitch, leaving a 4-inch (10.2 cm) opening along the bottom edge. Clip the corners and curves, and turn right side out.

6 Stuff the pillow lightly. Slipstitch the opening closed.

7 Hand-sew the remaining ribbon to the upper corners of the pillow to make a handle for hanging. For a whimsical touch, loop the ribbon at the corners then secure the loops with a tiny knot.

hearts on a string

Love comes in many forms, but a heart shape speaks clearly, without reservation. You can even skip the final step and give a gift with no strings attached!

DESIGNER

HANNA ANDERSSON

WHAT YOU NEED

Basic sewing tools

2 fabric scraps, any color, 4¼ x 4¾ inches (11 x 12 cm)

Thread in matching color

Stuffing material

Ribbon or household yarn

Big sewing needle (for ribbon or yarn)

WHAT YOU DO

1 Draw or copy a heart-shaped pattern onto scrap paper and cut it out. Make sure the shape fits onto your fabric scraps. Place the paper pattern on the wrong side of one fabric piece and pin it in place.

2 With the pencil, draw around the edges of the pattern onto the fabric. Remove the pattern, but don't cut the fabric yet. Pin the two fabric pieces together, right sides facing. Place the pins within the heart shape.

3 Sew the fabric pieces together, following the pattern line. If you're using a sewing machine, pivot the fabric to turn sharp corners. Leave about ¾ inch (2 cm) open so you can turn your heart right side out.

4 Cut out the fabric heart, about ¼ inch (6 mm) from the seam. Cut small notches into the seam allowance so it will lie flat when it's turned.

5 Turn the heart shape right side out. Push out all edges using the non-sharp end of the pencil. Stuff it full through the gap with small pieces of the stuffing material. Hand sew along the two edges of the gap to close it, using small stitches.

6 Use the bigger needle to attach the thin ribbon or household yarn at the top of your heart to hang it up.

TAKE THIS TO HEART

This project won't break your bank. Since you need only tiny pieces of any fabric, you don't have to buy anything new. Just recycle your old scraps!

undercover portfolio

DESIGNER

LISA COX

WHAT YOU NEED

Basic sewing tools

¾ yard (68.6 cm) or 3 fat quarters of quilting cotton in three patterns (A, B, and C)

2 pieces of fusible interfacing, 10 x 18 inches (25.4 x 45.7 cm) and 2½ x 18 inches (6.4 x 45.7 cm)

Satin piping, 18 inches (45.7 cm) in length

Thread in matching colors

Lightweight batting, 12 x18 inches (30.5 x 45.7 cm)

Rickrack, 18 inches (45.7 cm) in length

1-inch-wide (2.5 cm) masking tape

2 zippers, each 12 inches (30.5 cm) in length

2 sheets of clear plastic, each 7½ x 12 inches (19 x 30.5 cm)

⅜-inch (1 cm) satin ribbon, 70 inches (177.8 cm) in length

Small drinking glass

¾-inch (1.9 cm) satin bias tape, 60 inches (152.4 cm) in length

¾-inch (1.9 cm) button

Here's the gift no one has, but everyone will want. Will a bride appreciate this special case for carrying special lingerie on her special honeymoon trip? Oh yes, she will.

WHAT YOU DO

1 Cut each of the patterned fabrics as follows:

Pattern A: 10 x 18 inches (25.4 x 45.7 cm)

Pattern B: two pieces at 2½ x 18 inches (6.4 x 45.7 cm)

Pattern C: 10 x 18 inches (25.4 x 45.7 cm)

2 Iron the interfacing onto the Pattern A piece and one of the Pattern B pieces. Sandwich the piping between the two, right sides together with the corded edge inward. Sew all three together close to the piping with the zipper foot. Press the seams to one side. Set this piece aside.

BEHAVIOR PATTERN

While you can choose any complementary colors to create this present, the designer used an orange, cream, and pink design (Pattern A); a pink and orange spotted pattern (Pattern B); and a pink and cream floral (Pattern C). Choose fabrics you know your recipient will love; just make sure the binding, rickrack, ribbon, thread, and zippers match.

3 Place the second Pattern B piece and the Pattern C piece together, right sides facing, and sew along the long side, using a ¼-inch (6 mm) seam allowance. Press the seams to one side. Layer this piece on top of the batting and pin it in place. Machine-quilt them together using a 1-inch (2.5 cm) crosshatch pattern. Sew the rickrack along the junction of the two fabrics.

4 Overlap one of the zippers with the long edge of one of the plastic sheets and pin in place. Baste them together. Lay a 12-inch (30.5 cm) length of ribbon over the basted edge, and sew one edge over the zipper (with a zipper foot) and the other over the plastic sheet. Repeat for the other zipper and plastic sheet, using another 12-inch (30.5 cm) length of ribbon.

5 Lay both plastic sheets on top of the quilted lining piece, zippers toward the middle so the zippers are about 1 inch (2.5 cm) apart, and pin them all together close to the edges (figure 1). Lay another 12-inch (30.5 cm) length of ribbon over the inside exposed edge of the zipper and sew along both long edges to secure the zipper to the lining. Repeat for the other zipper.

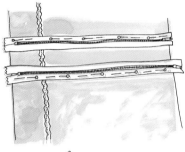

figure 1

MASKING SCHEME

To help you sew the diagonal crosshatch pattern, place a strip of masking tape at a 45° angle over the fabric as a guide when you machine-quilt. Sew one line at a time, moving the tape as needed.

6 Place the lining with zippered pockets on top of the outside cover, wrong sides together. Baste in place around the perimeter, close to the edge. Use the drinking glass as a template to draw rounded corners and then trim each corner, cutting through all layers.

7 With the outside cover face up, place two pieces of 11-inch (27.9 cm) ribbon in the middle of one side edge and baste it in place. Fold one end of the bias tape under ½ inch (1.3 cm), and then wrap it around the entire periphery, pinning it in place as you go. Sew it down through all layers, being careful not to sew through the zipper ends.

8 Sew the button to the opposite edge of the outside cover from the 11-inch (27.9 cm) ribbon. Fold the portfolio in half, and then tie the ribbon around the button to secure it.

wake, rattle & stroll

DESIGNER

ROXANNE BEAUVAIS

*P*laced around the wrist or clutched in a chubby little hand, this flowery rattle gives a new mom the greatest gift of all: a quiet and happy baby.

WHAT YOU NEED

Basic sewing tools

Petal pattern (page 296)

3 coordinating or contrasting cotton fabrics, each 6 x 8 inches (15.2 x 20.3 cm)

White thread

Polyester fiberfill

24 jingle bells, each ⅜ inch (1 cm)

Safety Pin

⅜-inch (1 cm) wide elastic, 8 inches (20.3 cm) in length

HIDE AND SEEK

To keep the elastic hidden even when stretched, hand stitch the petals together with matching thread. A couple of quick stitches on both sides of each petal will do the trick.

WHAT YOU DO

1 Cut out four pattern pieces in each fabric, totaling twelve petals.

2 Pin two matching petals, right sides together. Mark 1 inch (2.5 cm) down on either side of the petal. Sew around the petal from marked spot to marked spot with a ½-inch (1.3 cm) seam allowance. Keep the needle down when you shift the fabric around the curve.

3 Notch the seam allowance around the curve, and then turn the petal right side out. Press it flat. Tuck the raw edges in as you iron so the sides are even all the way up. Fold the straight edges down ¼ inch (6 mm) on the short end and press.

4 Stuff fiberfill and four jingle bells into the petal up to the marked 1-inch (2.5 cm) point. Pin the petal at the marked point and topstitch across. Sew another seam as close to the top straight edge as possible, creating a casing.

5 Repeat steps 2 through 4 to create five more petals, making sure to use different fabrics.

6 Arrange the petals in an alternating fabric pattern. Attach the safety pin to the end of the elastic and thread it through the casing of each petal in turn. Pull the elastic tight to create a gathered effect (see the photo at left).

7 Pin and sew the ends of the elastic together several times. Distribute the petals evenly around the elastic.

"I do"

When all the details of the special wedding day
are given such care, why not create a one-of-a-kind keepsake
ring bearer pillow that can be treasured for years to come?
A simple ribbon tie keeps the rings securely in place.

DESIGNER

ELIZABETH HARTMAN

WHAT YOU NEED

Basic sewing tools

¼ yard (22.8 cm) of silk dupioni

¼ yard (22.8 cm) of a coordinating cotton print

2 blanks for 1-inch (2.5 cm) covered buttons

2 squares of lightweight fusible interfacing, 9 x 9 inches (22.9 x 22.9 cm)

Polyester fiberfill

Water-soluble fabric marker

Embroidery floss

1 yard (.9 m) of ⅜-inch (9.5 mm) organdy ribbon

FOR THE OPTIONAL APPLIQUÉ

5-inch (12.7 cm) square of white wool felt

5-inch (12.7 cm) square of paper-backed fusible web

Thread to match

Black embroidery floss (optional)

SEAM ALLOWANCE

½ inch (1.3 cm) unless otherwise noted

FINISHED SIZE

9 x 9 inches (22.9 x 22.9 cm)

What You Cut

Silk Dupioni

- *1 square, 4 x 4 inches (10.2 x 10.2 cm)*
- *2 strips, each 1½ x 4 inches (3.8 x 10.2 cm)*
- *2 strips, each 1½ x 6 inches (3.8 x 15.2 cm)*
- *2 strips, each 2 x 6 inches (5.1 x 15.2 cm)*
- *2 strips, each 2 x 9 inches (5.1 x 22.9 cm)*

Cotton Print

- *Cut exactly the same as for the silk dupioni*

WHAT YOU DO

1 Cut the fabric as described in the box, above. Following the manufacturer's instructions, use scraps of the silk and cotton to cover the two button blanks, one in each fabric.

2 Follow figure 1 to piece the back of the pillow first. Placing right sides together, and using a ¼-inch (6 mm) seam allowance, sew one of the 1½ x 4-inch (3.8 x 10.2 cm) silk strips to the top and one to the bottom of the 4-inch (10.2 cm) cotton square. Press the seams open.

---

3 Sew the two 1½ x 6-inch (3.8 x 15.2 cm) silk strips to the left and right sides of the square, creating a frame around it. Repeat the same process by sewing the two 2 x 6-inch (5.1 x 15.2 cm) strips of printed cotton to the top and bottom of the block and the two 2 x 9-inch (5.1 x 22.9 cm) strips to the left and right sides.

4 Press all seams open. Fuse one of the squares of fusible interfacing to the wrong side of the pieced block.

figure 1

5 Make the front of the pillow by repeating steps 2 through 4. Your center square will be silk framed in printed cotton with an exterior frame of silk, as shown in figure 1.

6 With right sides together, stitch the front and back pillow panels together, leaving a 3-inch (7.6 cm) opening on one of the sides for turning.

7 Trim the corners and turn the pillow right side out. Push out the corners if needed. Use the fiberfill to stuff the pillow to the desired fullness, and hand-stitch the opening closed.

8 Use a ruler and soluble marker to lightly mark the center point of both the front and back of the pillow. Thread a long sewing needle with approximately 18 inches (45.7 cm) of embroidery floss. Using the covered buttons, follow the instructions on page 23 for tufting a pillow.

9 Tie the organdy ribbon around the silk-covered button on the pillow's front and trim as desired.

OPTIONAL APPLIQUÉ

1 After completing step 5 for the pillow, copy the template on page 297 and cut it out. Use it to trace the shape onto the paper side of the fusible web. Press to fuse the web to the wrong side of the felt. Allow to cool and cut out the bird.

2 Remove the paper and position the appliqué in the top left corner of the front pillow panel, with its beak approximately 1½ inches (3.8 cm) from the center of the pillow. You want the bird to appear as if it's carrying the ribbon with the rings. Once you're satisfied with the appliqué's location, cover the area with a scrap cloth or lightweight towel and press it in place.

3 Use the zigzag, satin, or buttonhole stitch on your machine to carefully sew around the edges of the appliqué. If desired, use the black embroidery floss to stitch an eye on the bird. Then finish the pillow as above.

use

home sweet home 142
nifty fifties 144
no-sew kitsch 148
sew on the go 150
now and zen 152
dress it up 154
retro active 157
yo-yo go 160
bee sewing 162
picnic partner 165
making the band 168
pocket placemats 170
girly garden 173
pinning zoo 176
all buttoned up 178
salsa softies 180

ribbon rounds 182
scorchin' 185
log in 188
cute+curious 191
dot's diner 194
new neutral 196
eco on-the-go 198
corsage pins 201
close-knit friends 204
sweet treat 206
belt it out 208
pin pals 210
whipstitch it good 213
trupunto trio 215
spot on 218

homesweethome
coasters

*P*rotect your coffee table
in style with these down-home
coasters. Made from felt and fabric
remnants, these coasters can be
pieced together in a flash.

DESIGNER

WENDY ARACICH

WHAT YOU NEED

Basic sewing tools

Remnants of three coordinating fabrics

Thread

¼ yard (22.9 cm) wool felt

Utility knife

Embroidery floss

Embroidery needle

SEAM ALLOWANCE

¼ inch (0.6 cm)

WHAT YOU DO

1 Cut 3½ x 1-inch (8.9 x 2.5 cm) rectangular strips from the coordinating fabrics for a total of 64 strips. Cut eight 4¾ x 4¾-inch (12 x 12 cm) squares of felt.

2 Arrange strips vertically (longer sides together) into eight rows of eight rectangular strips. Join strips one row at a time, starting by pinning the right edge

of the first strip to the left edge of the second strip, with right sides together. Next, pin the right edge of the second strip to the left edge of the third strip. Repeat until all strips in a row are pinned. Set aside, and repeat with the remaining rows.

3 Machine stitch along the pinned edges. Press seams open.

4 Pair stitched rows, and stitch the bottom of the top row to the top of the bottom row. Repeat with remaining rows to make a total of four pairs. Machine stitch along pinned edges. Press seams open.

5 On the wrong side of four pieces of felt, center the template (see the template on page 300) and trace with the pencil. Using the rotary cutter or a utility knife, cut out shapes carefully along the traced lines, and take care not to cut through the area outside of the traced line.

6 Pin patchwork, right side up, to the underside of the cut felt. Adjust the placement of the felt to compose your patchwork within the house shape. Don't worry if the patchwork extends beyond the sides of the coasters.

7 With the embroidery floss, sew a running stitch around the perimeter of the house shapes, ¼ inch (0.6 cm) from the edge, and take care to catch the patchwork with the stitches. Turn the coaster over, and carefully trim the patchwork about ½ inch (1.3 cm) outside the stitches.

8 Pin the coaster back to the front, wrong sides together. Machine stitch around the perimeter. Repeat with the remaining coasters.

nifty fifties

$\mathcal{T}$hink June Cleaver with far more sass! This charming potholder and oven mitt set mixes '50s-style fabrics with cute, contemporary flair.

DESIGNER

AUTUM HALL

144

WHAT YOU NEED

Basic sewing tools

Up to 1/4 yard (22.9 cm) each of cotton fabric scraps in red and aqua or any combination

1/4 yard (22.9 cm) natural-colored linen fabric

1/4 yard (22.9 cm) fleece

12 x 20 inch (30.5 x 50.8 cm) piece of heavy canvas in a light color

4-inch (10.2 cm) square of red gingham

Rotary cutter

Cutting mat

White thread

Black embroidery floss

Embroidery needle

Seam ripper

Chopstick

Aqua button

Fusible tape (optional)

WHAT YOU DO

FOR THE POTHOLDER

1 Referring to the chart below, cut the fabric pieces.

2 Referring to figure 1 for placement, stitch pieces 1, 2, and 3 together sequentially. Press each seam open and then to the side with a 1/4-inch (0.6 cm) seam allowance. Stitch this strip to piece 4, and set aside.

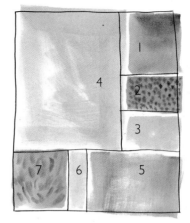

figure 1

Retro kitchen print	Piece #1: 4-inch (10.2 cm) square Piece #5: 4 x 5-inch (10.2 x 12.7 cm) rectangle
Red and white print	Piece #2: 4 x 2-inch (10.2 x 5.1 cm) Strap: 2 x 4 inches (5.1 x 10.2 cm)
Solid aqua	Pieces #3 and #6: each 4 x 2 inches (10.2 x 5.1 cm)
Blue and green floral	Piece #7: 4-inch (10.2 cm) square
Linen	Piece #4: 6½-inch (16.5 cm) square Back: 10-inch (25.4 cm) square
Red gingham	Yo-yo: circle 4 inches (10.2 cm) in diameter
Fleece	2 pieces, 10 x 10 inches (25.4 x 25.4 cm)

3 Stitch pieces 5, 6, and 7 together sequentially. After pressing each seam open and to one side, stitch this strip to the block made in step 2.

4 Copy the teapot design on page 296. Transfer it to the lower right-hand corner of the linen square using a temporary-ink marking pen or pencil. Embroider it, using a backstitch for the outline of the teapot and steam. Satin stitch the heart.

5 Place the potholder top on top of the two layers of fleece. Use straight pins to hold it in place for machine quilting. With a long, straight machine stitch, topstitch close to the seam line on one side of each seam. Trim excess fleece from the edges, and square up if necessary.

6 To make the hanging tab from the 2 x 4-inch (5.1 x 10.2 cm) piece of fabric, fold the scrap in half the long way and press it. Then open and fold each long side in to the center and press. Fold in half to enclose the raw edges, and stitch down the open side. Fold in half, and pin in place at the upper right corner, about a ½ inch (1.3 cm) in from the right edge.

7 Place the 10-inch (25.4 cm) linen square over the pot-holder top, right sides together. Pin in place around all four sides. Sew around all sides, and leave a place on one side for turning right side out 3 to 4 inches (7.6-10.2 cm).

8 Clip the corners, and turn right side out through the opening. Push out the corners with the chopstick. Press neatly, and pin the opening closed. Secure it with a hidden stitch.

9 Cut a 4-inch (10.2 cm) circle from the red gingham for a yo-yo. Make a yo-yo, and stitch it to the corner of the potholder, sewing only through the front fabric and batting.

NOW YOU SEE IT...

By using disappearing ink, you can remove any marks not covered by the embroidery floss.

FOR THE MITT

1 Cut the fabric:

8 to 10 fabric scraps, 2 to 4 inches (5.1 to 10.2 cm) long x 4 inches (10.2 cm) wide

8 to 10 fabric scraps, various widths x 3 inches (7.6 cm) long for binding strip

Strip of red gingham, 2 x 20 inches (5.1 x 50.8 cm)

Strip for hang tab, 2 x 4 inches (5.1 x 10.2 cm)

Rectangle from linen, 6½ x 20 inches (16.5 x 50.8 cm)

Rectangle from fleece, 12 x 20 inches (30.5 x 50.8 cm)

Rectangle from canvas, 12 x 20 inches (30.5 x 50.8 cm)

2 Sew enough of the fabric strips together to make a piece about 20 inches (50.8 cm) long. Press seams to one side. Attach this patchwork strip to the gingham along one long side, and on the other long side attach the linen.

3 To make the binding, sew strips together to create a patchwork piece 3 x 15 inches (7.6 x 38.1 cm). Press the seams

to one side, and fold it in half the long way, wrong sides together. Set aside. Make the hang tab. Set aside.

4 To prepare the patchwork for quilting, make a sandwich with the canvas on bottom, fleece in the center, and patchwork on top, right side up.

5 Machine-quilt with a long machine stitch in a random pattern. Fold the quilted fabric in half, right sides together, and be sure the seam between the linen and patchwork matches up. Cut out the oven mitt shape using the pattern. Stitch up the thumb side only to the top of the thumb. Open up, and pin the binding to the right side of the mitt along the bottom edge, raw edges together.

6 Stitch the binding to the mitt with a ⅜-inch (1 cm) seam allowance. Fold the binding around to the back and press. Pin in place to secure for stitching.

7 Stitch in place by stitching in the ditch, or stitching from the front side right at the seam line so the stitching is nearly invisible. Pin the hang tab in place on the open side near the bottom. Be sure to pin it so the raw edge of the tab is even with the raw edge of the mitt. Turn the right sides together, and finish stitching around the mitt.

8 Trim the seams, and clip to the seam line at the V between the thumb and hand section. Turn right side out, using the chopstick if needed to push the thumb out.

PRACTICE ATTACHMENT

Use a glue stick to hold the layers together for stitching. Apply glue to each layer, and press with a hot iron to set.

no-sewkitsch

These vintage adorables offer no-stitch kitsch in just minutes. They're a great use for wonderful old pieces that don't fit your style in the kitchen, but will be a charm in your sewing room.

DESIGNER

AMY KAROL

WHAT YOU NEED

Basic sewing tools

Vintage teacup, eggcup, or small bowl

Glue stick

Decorative fabric

Vintage trims and notions

Hot glue and glue gun

WHAT YOU DO

1 Using your teacup as a guide, make a ball of polyester fiberfill double the size of the cup opening. Wrap the fabric tightly around the ball of stuffing and test fit it in the teacup. It should fit snugly and fluff up at the top.

2 Remove the ball from the cup, and adjust the stuffing as necessary for a tight fit. Tie a long piece of thread around the ends of the fabric to cinch it together, as tying string to a balloon. Trim off the excess fabric.

3 Use a hot glue gun to line the inside and bottom of the cup with glue. Carefully place the fabric ball into the cup, pressing firmly, and let the glue cool and dry.

4 Using a glue stick, secure ribbon around the cup, if desired. Add trims and vintage buttons with pins on top.

Oblong Variation

If your vintage piece is rectangular, form the stuffing in step 1 into an oblong or tube shape. Then, wrap the fabric around the stuffing, like wrapping a present. Secure the fabric with hot glue, rather than thread. Then proceed with steps 3 and 4.

GLASS CHOICES

Look for opaque glass vintage items to turn into pincushions. Opaque glass will mask the fabric, thread, and glue tucked inside.

sewonthego

This traveling kit can go where you go and serve you on the fly with a tube the perfect size for buttons, needles, thread, and a custom-made, pop-out pincushion.

DESIGNER

AMY ALBARRÁN

WHAT YOU NEED

Basic sewing tools

Fabric

Bead storage tube with a
1³/₈-inch opening

Silicone craft glue

¹/₄-inch hole punch

Buttons or embellishments

Sewing notions

WHAT YOU DO

1 Cut a 3¹/₂-inch diameter circle of fabric, and hand sew a running stitch along the edge with a ¹/₄-inch seam allowance for a drawstring.

2 Pull both ends of the drawstring, gathering the fabric into a ball form. Stuff the sack firmly with polyester fiberfill. Draw the thread tight, and secure it with a knot to close.

3 Remove the cap from the bead storage tube, cutting off any plastic loop from the top of the cap. Dab silicone craft glue inside the cap, and spread it along the inside rim, staying clear of the edge.

4 Place the ball inside the cap, pressing it against the sides for a snug fit. Set a weight on top of the cushion for about 15 minutes to set the glue.

5 Use a ¹/₄-inch hole punch to clip two half-circle notches into the rim of the tube on opposite sides. This gives finger grip areas for popping off the cap.

6 Dress up your kit by gluing a stack of buttons, or other embellishments, on top of the cap. Just make sure they are flat so the pincushion can sit on its base when you're using it.

7 Let the glue cure overnight. Then, stash notions like safety pins, extra buttons, needle and thread, and even a thimble in your kit. You're ready to go!

now and zen

The fresh, clean lines and minimal design of this potholder may inspire you to ponder the meaning of life while you wait for your brownies to finish baking.

DESIGNER

MAITREYA DUNHAM

WHAT YOU NEED

Basic sewing tools

8 strips of coordinating fabric for the patchwork, each 4 x 1½ inches (10.2 x 3.8 cm)

Solid-colored fabric for the front, 5¼ x 8½ inches (13.3 x 21.6 cm)

Solid fabric for the back, 8½ inches (21.6 cm) square

Circular object—such as a bowl—to trace, 8½ inches (21.6 cm) in diameter

Piece of batting, 8½ inches (21.6 cm) square

2 feet (61 cm) of double-fold bias tape, ½ inch (1.3 cm) wide

SEAM ALLOWANCE

¼ inch (0.6 cm)

WHAT YOU DO

1 Design the patchwork section by arranging the strips, with long edges matching, to form a pleasing design. Stitch the strips together along the long edges. Press the seams open.

2 Sew the long side of the patchwork to the long side of the solid-colored front piece, right sides together, to make the top. Press open the seam.

3 Trace a circle on the top, centering it. (The entire circle should fit with a little extra space around the edges.) Align a ruler along each seam of the patchwork, and draw straight lines extending from the patchwork seam across the solid fabric.

4 Place the fabric for the back piece on your work surface, right side down. Stack the batting over it, and on top of that, place the patchwork piece right side up.

5 Pin all the layers together, close to the central line drawn in step 3. Machine stitch along the line. Remove the pins, and smooth the layers. Pin near the adjacent line, stitch, and repeat until all the lines have been stitched.

6 Cut around the traced circle. Pin the bias tape to both the top and bottom sides of the potholder, all around the raw edge. Once you've pinned around the entire circle, leave an additional loose tail of tape 9 inches (22.9 cm) long at the end, then cut off any extra material. (You'll use the tail later to create a loop for hanging the potholder.) Sew just the tail of tape closed, using a narrow zigzag stitch.

7 Create the loop by tucking the zigzagged end of the tail underneath the tape that's pinned around the circle. Use a zigzag stitch to fasten the bias tape all around the potholder.

IN STITCHES

Nothing says you have to use straight stitches to sew down bias tape. Most sewing machines have at least a few fancy stitches from which to choose. Use one of them to add another level of embellishment.

dress*it*up

Charming and girlish, this paper-doll dress pincushion will transport you back to childhood.

DESIGNER

NATHALIE MORNU

WHAT YOU NEED

Basic sewing tools

Fabric, three prints, ¼ yard each

Fusible interfacing (one-sided)

Iron and ironing board

Muslin, ¼ yard

Sewing machine (optional)

String

WHAT YOU DO

1 Cut a 6 x 10-inch rectangle from the main fabric for the pincushion. Cut two 4-inch diameter circles from the second fabric for the top and base of the pincushion. Use this second fabric for the dress as well in step 2. Set the cut pieces aside.

2 Place the interfacing, adhesive side up, on an ironing board, and lay the remaining portion of the dress fabric, right side up, on top of it. Press with an iron to adhere them, according to the directions on the interfacing package.

3 Cut a 4 x 4-inch square of the third fabric, and repeat step 2 with the square.

4 Make a pattern from the template (page 297), and cut three of dress A from the main fabric with the interfacing backing. Cut three collar shapes, six cuffs, and three waistbands from the 4 x 4-inch square with the interfacing backing. Cut three of dress B from the muslin.

5 Pin each dress A onto a muslin dress B, leaving an even border of muslin all around.

6 Pin the dresses side by side and evenly spaced onto the rectangle cut in step 1. Keep them at least one inch from each end. Hand stitch the dresses in place, sewing close to the edge of dress A.

7 Pin the collars, cuffs, and waistbands to the dresses, and hand stitch them in place as well.

8 Pin the shorter edges of the rectangle, right sides together, and machine stitch, or hand sew, the seam. This is the body of the pincushion. Set aside.

USABLE FUSIBLE

Take care when using fusible interfacing so that your iron does not touch the adhesive side or it's goodbye shiny, smooth iron and hello burned, sticky mess. If your fabric does not completely cover the interfacing, cut the interfacing down to size to prevent any mishaps.

9 To make the piping, cut four 1½-inch-wide strips of the third fabric (used for the collar and cuffs) on the diagonal. Stitch pairs of the strips together along the narrow ends to make two strips that each measure longer than 10 inches. Fold each strip in half lengthwise, wrong sides together, and press along the fold with your fingers.

10 Cut two pieces of string 12 inches long, and stretch one inside the furrow of each folded strip. Machine or hand baste the strips closed.

11 With the body of the pincushion still inside out from step 8, pin a piping strip completely around the bottom edge on the right side, matching the raw edges.

12 Carefully open up the ends of the piping and clip the inside string to the exact length of the circumference of the pincushion. Close the piping back up, overlapping the ends and turning the outer end under, cutting off any excess. Baste the piping to the pincushion and remove the pins.

13 Repeat steps 11 and 12 with the other piece of piping, sewing it to the top edge of the pincushion.

14 Leaving the pincushion inside out, pin one of the fabric circles from step 2 to the bottom of the pincushion, right sides together. Baste in place and remove the pins.

15 Using a zipper foot, or hand sewing, stitch all the way around the bottom of the pincushion, stitching in the "ditch" of the piping—as close to the string as possible.

16 Repeat steps 14 and 15 to attach the top piece, leaving a 2-inch gap to turn the fabric right side out.

17 Turn the fabric right side out and stuff it firmly with polyester fiberfill, using the eraser end of a pencil to help work the stuffing into the corners. Hand stitch the opening closed.

CUTTING ON THE DIAGONAL

To cut a piece on the diagonal, or on the "bias," cut at a 45° angle to the selvage edge. The cut piece will have more give and flexibility to wrap around corners and curve when used for piping. (Perhaps a metaphor for life for those who feel they're always going against the grain.)

*retro*active

$\mathcal{T}$he appeal of this retro little potholder comes from mixing a vintage tea towel with pretty, contemporary prints.

DESIGNER

SARAH MCDOUGALL

WHAT YOU NEED

Basic sewing tools

Fat quarter of each of four coordinating pieces of fabric

Piece of fabric from a vintage tea towel

Piece of number fabric

Pink thread

Sewing machine with straight and zigzag stitch

⅓ yard (30.5 cm) batting

6½-inch (16.5 cm) piece of ribbon, red or color of your choice

White thread

Rickrack

SWEET TWEET

Tea towels like this one sell for a song in antique stores and thrift shops.

WHAT YOU DO

1 Cut a piece of ribbon 6½ inches (16.5 cm) long, and a piece of rickrack also 6½ inches (16.5 cm) long. Prewash and iron all the fabrics, then cut them to the measurements in the chart below.

2 Sew the fabric's right sides together, starting with sewing the bird fabric to the bottom fabric. Then sew the side fabric to the fabric you just sewed. Sew the top fabric to the previously sewn fabrics. Press each seam with an iron after sewing.

3 Fold over all sides of the number fabric, and press to prevent fraying. Pin the pressed number to the front piece of the potholder. Using the pink thread, zigzag around the number fabric to fasten it down.

4 Place the top fabric of the potholder on the batting, and cut around the edges, leaving a ½-inch (1.3 cm) seam allowance.

Do this twice more so you'll have three layers of batting, and once again for the bottom fabric of the potholder.

5 With the top and bottom fabrics of the potholder right sides together, add the three layers of batting over top.

6 Fold the ribbon in half, and insert the folded edge between the fabric that's right sides together. Pin. Leave some of the ribbon's rough edge out to make the seam easier to sew.

7 Using the top layer of fabric as a guide, sew around three of the sides completely. On the fourth side, leave a 3-inch (7.6 cm) opening in the middle. Back tack the start and finish of each seam.

Top fabric	8 x 2 inches (20.3 x 5.1 cm)
Side fabric	3 x 7 inches (7.6 x 17.8 cm)
Bottom fabric	6½ x 2¾ inches (16.5 x 7 cm)
Bird fabric	4½ x 6½ inches (11.4 x 16.5 cm)
Number fabric	Cut out the number, leaving a ½-inch (1.3 cm) seam allowance around it

8 Trim excess batting and fabric on the three completely sewn sides. On the opening, leave about a 1/2 inch (1.3 cm) of batting and 1 inch (2.5 cm) of fabric, so it will be easier to close and hand-sew the seam. Turn inside out and press.

9 Tuck in the fabric opening and hand-sew. Machine sew the rickrack. Back tack both ends.

10 Quilt the potholder by sewing around the number and the birds, and add your own designs to make it unique.

EDGING IN

You can use a running stitch with embroidery floss in a contrasting color for a decorative stitch, or make tiny stitches with thread in the same color as the fabric if you want them to be hidden—or, use a combination of both.

yo-yogo

*T*he best trick to this potholder embellished with yo-yos? After pulling a pie out of the oven, you can set it aside to cool and really go walk the dog.

DESIGNER

DORIE BLAISDELL SCHWARZ

WHAT YOU NEED

Basic sewing tools

¼ yard (22.9 cm) white cotton fabric

Green fabric scraps at least 5 inches (12.7 cm) long

Bright pink fabric scraps

Cup or another round object for tracing

Cotton batting, 7 x 14 inches (17.8 x 35.6 cm)

White thread

Medium turquoise rickrack

Green thread

SEAM ALLOWANCE

¼ inch (0.6 cm)

WHAT YOU DO

1 Cut one 7½-inch (19 cm) square of white cotton, then cut one 4 x 7½-inch (10.2 x 19 cm) rectangle of white cotton.

2 Cut the green scraps into strips about 5 inches (12.7 cm) long in varying widths, some at an angle.

3 Use a cup with a diameter of 3¼ inches (8.3 cm) to trace five circles on the wrong side of the pink fabric scraps, and cut out the circles. Cut two 6¾-inch (17.1 cm) squares of cotton batting.

4 To sew the grass, line up the green strips randomly, and arrange the angled strips to complement each other and make a straight line in the end. With white thread in the machine, stitch one green scrap to another, starting from one end.

When the sewn grass looks about 8 inches (20.3 cm) long, stop and press, pressing the seam allowance to the darker fabric where possible.

5 Trim the grass to 7½ x 4 inches (19 x 10.2 cm). Sew the white rectangle to the grass, and press the seam toward the grass.

6 Make yo-yos out of the pink circles.

7 Pin the yo-yos to the potholder front. Evenly space three yo-yos directly above the grass, and stagger the other two in a row above. Sew the yo-yos to the fabric using a running stitch and catch just the back part of the yo-yo.

8 To assemble, pin the rickrack to the potholder front, matching edges. Then pin the back of the potholder to the front, right sides facing each other.

9 Stitch around the edge of the potholder, leaving a 3-inch (7.6 cm) opening. Clip the corners and turn. Slide the double layer of cotton batting into the opening. Smooth the batting, and stitch the opening closed.

10 Quilt the potholder by machine-stitching around the yo-yos and up and down the grass strips. To quilt on top of the green fabric, switch the thread color to green, but leave the bobbin white.

beesewing

beehive
pincushion

WHAT YOU NEED

Basic sewing tools

8 x 10-inch wool felt, gold

Wool felt scrap, dark brown

Embroidery floss, gold, bright gold, dark brown

WHAT YOU DO

1 Make a pattern from the template (page 300). Use the pattern to cut two hive pieces and one base from the gold felt. Cut one door from the dark brown felt.

2 Stitch the door to the bottom center of one of the hive pieces using small running stitches and two strands of dark brown floss.

3 Lay the hive pieces with wrong sides together. Using a whipstitch and three strands of gold floss, stitch them together along the sides, leaving the bottom open.

4 Thread and knot the needle with six long strands of dark brown floss (long enough to wrap around the hive five or six

The only things sweeter than this little hive for your sewing basket are the honeybee pins you make to go with it. You won't want to sew with ordinary pins again.

DESIGNER

CASSIE GRIFFIN

times). Bring the threaded needle up through the inside of the hive and out near the top; leave a 2-inch tail inside the hive.

5 Repeat step 4 using four long strands of bright gold floss, bringing it out next to the brown floss. Leave the gold and brown strands hanging until step 7.

6 Stuff the hive lightly with polyester fiberfill to make embroidering easier—you'll add more stuffing later.

7 Using a couching stitch and the brown and bright gold threads, wrap and stitch around the hive five or six times. Space the brown wraps 1/2-inch apart and secure them with the gold thread. At the door, just slide the needle and thread behind the brown felt and continue stitching on the other side.

8 Whipstitch the base onto the hive using three strands of gold floss, leaving a 1 1/2-inch opening to finish stuffing.

9 Stuff firmly until the pincushion is about three-quarters full. Finish stuffing with rice or lentils to give the cushion weight. Then sew up the gap.

BEE PRETTY

For an even prettier finish, leave the needle and thread hanging when you stop to stuff. After topping off with rice or lentils for weight, pick up the needle and continue whipstitching to close the gap.

bee pins

WHAT YOU NEED

Clear shrink plastic

Straight pins

Bee paper punch

High-quality colored pencils, yellow, white, black

Thick rag or hot pad

Fine-grain sandpaper

Baking sheet

Oven

WHAT YOU DO

1 Rough the shrink plastic with fine-grain sandpaper to help the pencil color adhere in the next step.

2 Using the bee punch, make bees from the sanded plastic. Use the pencils to fill in the bees with color.

3 Put the bees colored side down on a thick rag or hot pad. Push a straight pin completely through the middle of one bee. Repeat for all bees.

4 Place the bees on a cookie sheet with the pin sticking straight up.

5 Shrink the bee pins in the oven according to the directions on the shrink plastic.

6 Remove them from the oven, and let them cool. Then swarm your hive with bees!

PINS OF A DIFFERENT COLOR

Choose a different theme for your pins—ladybugs, animals, or stars and moons—and follow the Bee Pins instructions to customize pins to every whim.

picnic partner

Linen and absorbent cotton make wonderful napkins, and a complementary fabric box stores them away neatly until the next time you dine under the sun or stars.

WHAT YOU NEED

Basic sewing tools

1¼ yards (114.3 cm) of printed fabric

1¼ yards (114.3 cm) of linen

Embroidery hoop

Embroidery needle

One skein of embroidery thread to match printed fabric

Sewing thread to match embroidery thread

¼ yard (22.9 cm) of heavy-weight interfacing

1 yard (91.4 cm) of matching ribbon or fabric strip, ½ inch (1.3 cm) wide

DESIGNER

STEPHANIE COSTO

WHAT YOU DO

MAKING THE NAPKINS

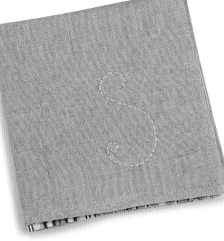

1 Cut six 13-inch (33 cm) squares of the print fabric. (If you're using two separate prints, cut three squares of each.) Cut six more 13-inch (33 cm) squares of the linen.

2 With the fabric pen, write initials (such as those of the planned recipient) at the bottom right corner of each piece of linen. Place one piece in the embroidery hoop and embroider over the initials, using a backstitch and six strands of embroidery thread in a color that matches the print fabric. Repeat for the remaining five linen pieces.

3 Place one linen and one printed fabric square right sides together. Sew the sides using a ½-inch (1.3 cm) seam allowance,

leaving a 2-inch (5.1 cm) opening on one side. Trim the seam and clip the corners, being careful not to clip through the stitching. Turn the fabric right side out and press the fabric so the seams lie flat.

4 Using a thread color that matches the embroidery, top stitch around all sides of the square, ¼ inch (6 mm) from the edge, making sure to close the opening.

5 Repeat steps 3 and 4 to make the remaining five napkins.

MAKING THE NAPKIN BOX

6 Cut a 13½-inch (34.3 cm) square from the printed fabric. Cut a 3¼-inch (8.3 cm) square out of each corner.

7 Fold each corner together along the cut, right sides together. Pin and sew the edges using a ½-inch (1.3 cm) seam allowance (figure 1). Trim the seams.

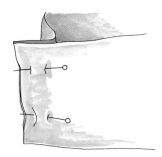

figure 1

8 Repeat steps 6 and 7 with the linen fabric, except for two things: fold the corners wrong sides together and leave a 1½-inch opening in one of the corners.

YOUR PRINT IS SHOWING

If you decide to use only one printed fabric, get the full amount (1¼ yards [114.3 cm]). If, however, you want to use two different printed fabrics, get ¾ yard (68.6 cm) of one and ½ yard (45.7 cm) of another.

9 Place the printed fabric inside the linen fabric so the right sides are together and the raw edges on top are even. Sew the fabrics together on the top raw edge using a ½-inch (1.3 cm) seam allowance. Trim the seams. Turn the fabric box right side out through the opening. Press the top edges to make the seam lie flat.

10 Cut a 6-inch (15.2 cm) piece of heavyweight interfacing. Roll it into a narrow tube and carefully insert it into the opening in the fabric box. Guide the interfacing so it lies flat on the bottom of the box.

11 Cut four 6 x 3¼-inch (15.2 x 8.3 cm) pieces of heavyweight interfacing. Using a wide zigzag stitch, sew the short sides together to form a four-sided box.

12 Roll the stitched sides into a long narrow tube. Insert it into the opening in the fabric box. Guide the sides of the heavyweight interfacing into the sides of the fabric box, matching up the corners. Press down the corners inside the box with your fingers.

13 Using a ¼-inch (6 mm) seam allowance and the thread color you used to top-stitch the fabric napkins, topstitch all around the top of the box. Slipstitch the opening by hand to close it.

PUTTING IT ALL TOGETHER

14 Fold each napkin into a 6-inch (15.2 cm) square and place it into the napkin box.

15 Tie a bow around the napkin box using the ribbon or fabric strip.

making the band

F lyaway hairs got you down? This simple headband with pretty buttons will tame any mane. An elastic underside makes it easy to wear so you don't need any pins to keep it in place.

DESIGNER

BETHANY MANN

WHAT YOU NEED

Basic sewing tools

Coordinating cotton prints, maximum size of any one print 4 x 6 inches (10.2 x 15.2 cm)

Thread, 2 colors to coordinate and contrast with fabrics

8 x 15-inch (20.3 x 38.1 cm) solid cotton for backing and elastic casing

Tailor's chalk

8 inches (20.3 cm) of 1-inch-wide (2.5 cm) elastic (preferably non-rolling)

Buttons: 3 small, 2 large

SEAM ALLOWANCE

¼ inch (0.6 cm)

WHAT YOU DO

1 Cut 10 assorted 2 x 4-inch (5.1 x 10.2 cm) strips with the rotary cutter and ruler. Arrange the pieces in a pattern you choose.

2 Seam each strip end-to-end on the 4-inch (10.2 cm) edge using coordinating thread. Press open all seams.

3 Cut a piece of solid cloth backing 4 x 15 inches (10.2 x 38.1 cm). Sew it along the long sides to the patchwork block with right sides facing. Press all the patchwork seams open.

4 Use the tailor's chalk and ruler to mark diagonal tapers on the last patch at each end. Mark diagonally from the seam to the fabric edge 1 inch (2.5 cm) in from the closest corner. Seam on these marks and trim to a ¼-inch (0.6 cm) seam allowance. Turn inside out and press.

5 Trim the remaining solid cotton to 12 x 4 inches (30.5 x 10.2 cm), and fold in half lengthwise. Seam the raw edges together down the long side. Turn inside out and press.

6 Topstitch half-channels on each edge with the contrasting thread, and leave a 1 x 8-inch (2.5 x 20.3 cm) channel down the middle. Ruche this center channel casing over the 8-inch (20.3 cm) length of no-roll elastic.

7 Pin ends into the opening on either end of the top part of the headband. Be sure to fold in and pin all raw edges. Try on carefully, and adjust size as necessary. Then double-seam the cased elastic in place to the headband top on each end.

8 To create the pleats where the headband top is seamed to the cased elastic band, fold the patchwork panel in half, and hand stitch a solid tack just beyond the edge of the attached elastic band. Then fold the patchwork panel open, and stitch a solid tack on each edge to keep it in place.

9 Sew the three small buttons on the third patch seam from the right, and sew the two large buttons on the fourth patch seam from the left.

169

pocket placemats

Here are some really cool placemats that have a pocket for silverware. This set of four allows you plenty of room for personalization.

WHAT YOU NEED

Basic sewing tools

1 yard (91.4 cm) of pre-washed fabric

Low-loft batting, 42 x 12 inches (106.7 x 30.5 cm)

¾ yard (68.6 cm) of prewashed accent fabric

Thread that matches both fabrics

Seam gauge (optional)

Skewer or point turner

SEAM ALLOWANCE

¼ inch (6 mm), unless otherwise noted

DESIGNER

LINDSEY M. HAHN

WHAT YOU DO

1 Cut the fabric to size, as follows:

Main fabric: 8 pieces, each 10½ x 12 inches (26.7 x 30.5 cm)

Batting: 4 pieces, each 10½ x 12 inches (26.7 x 30.5 cm)

Accent fabric: 8 pieces, each 6¼ x 3¾ inches (15.9 x 9.5 cm), and 5 pieces, each 2½ x 42 inches (6.4 x 106.7 cm)

2 With two small accent fabric rectangles, fold one short end over ½ inch (1.3 cm) and press. Pin the two right sides together, matching the folded edges. Stitch around the three raw edges using a ½-inch (1.3 cm) seam allowance, backstitching at the beginning and end. Trim the bottom corners and turn the pocket right side out. With the skewer or point turner, poke out the bottom corners neatly. Stitch the top folded edges together, using a ⅛-inch

(3 mm) seam allowance. Repeat to make three more pockets.

3 Mark three lines on one main fabric rectangle: 3 inches (7.6 cm), 6 inches (15.2 cm), and 9 inches (22.9 cm) from a short end. Layer the following: a different main fabric rectangle, right side down; one piece of batting; and the marked main fabric rectangle, right side up. Pin together all three layers, beginning in the middle. Following the lines, quilt stitch through all three layers, removing the pins as you sew. Repeat to make three more placemats.

4 Place the sewn pocket ½ inch (1.3 cm) from the bottom and from the right side of the placemat. Pin it in place. Starting in the upper right corner of the pocket, stitch the pocket to the mat, ⅛ inch (3 mm) from the pocket edge, ending in the

upper left corner. Backstitch at the beginning and end. Remove the pins. Repeat to attach the other three pockets.

5 To make double-long bias tape, layer one strip of accent fabric (right side up) and another right side down, creating a right angle. Draw a 45° line from corner to corner. Stitch along the line, backstitching at the beginning and end. Trim off the corner, leaving a seam allowance. Press the seam open, creating a straight piece of bias tape with an angled seam line. Repeat to make three more double-long strips.

6 Fold one bias strip in half lengthwise, wrong sides together, and press. Leaving at least 3 inches (7.6 cm) of a tail, sew the raw edges of the bias strip to the raw edge of the placemat, starting on a long side 2 inches (5.1 cm) from a corner. Pin the strip to the mat if necessary. Stop stitching ¼ inch (6 mm) from the next corner and backstitch. Fold the strip up, creating a 45° angle so that the unsewn strip is pointing away from you, in line with the side of the placemat (figure 1).

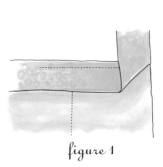

figure 1

7 Fold the strip back down, again lining up the raw edges, and attach it. Continue around the remaining three corners. Stop stitching and back tack less than 2 inches (5.1 cm) after the last corner. To create a nice seam at the end, smooth the two bias tails along the edge of the mat. Mark the point where they meet. Lay them together, right sides facing, and draw a 45° line. Pin the pieces in place and stitch down the line. Trim the corner, leaving a seam allowance. Align the raw edge of the bias tape to the last raw edge of the placemat and sew them together, backstitching at the beginning and end.

8 Fold the bias strip over to the back of the placemat, bringing the folded edge slightly past the stitch line. Pin the strip down and slipstitch the folded edge to the back of the mat. Make the stitches no more than ¼ inch (6 mm) apart. When you reach the first corner, fold it neatly onto itself, and then pin down the next edge before continuing. Work all the way around the placemat. When you return to where you started, knot the thread and trim it close.

9 Repeat steps 6 through 8 to finish the other three placemats.

girly garden

ℋow does this garden grow?
With appliquéd daisies,
French-knotted daffodils, and
beaded lilies, all in a row.

DESIGNER

JOAN K. MORRIS

WHAT YOU NEED

Basic sewing tools

12 x 12-inch (30.5 x 30.5 cm) square of green, purple, and blue cotton print

9 x 9-inch (22.9 x 22.9 cm) piece of green corduroy

2 pieces of felt, each 9 x 9 inches (22.9 x 22.9 cm)

2 pieces of green corduroy, 5½ x 7 inches (14 x 17.8 cm)

Assorted purple, pink, and orange cotton prints, each 3 x 3 inches (7.6 x 7.6 cm)

6 inches (15.2 cm) of light green rickrack, ½ inch (1.3 cm) wide

Matching green thread

Knitting needle

Iron-on adhesive

4 inches (10.2 cm) of pink plaid ribbon, ⅛ inch wide (0.3 cm)

4 inches (10.2 cm) of dark green rickrack, ⅛ inch (0.3 cm) wide

Invisible thread

Pink button

Green glass bead

Pink glass bead

Pink, purple, orange, and blue embroidery floss

Embroidery needle

WHAT YOU DO

1 Using scrap paper, make a 9-inch-square (22.9 x 22.9 cm) pattern. (Your piece will be 8 inches [20.3 cm] square after sewing.) Pin the pattern to the piece of green, purple, and blue cotton fabric on a diagonal, and cut it out. Cut out a piece of the 9 x 9-inch (22.9 x 22.9 cm) green corduroy and two pieces of felt the same size.

2 At one corner of the green, purple, and blue fabric, place the piece of light green rickrack, folded in half, for the handle. Place the fold toward the center and the raw edges into the corner. Baste in position.

3 Place the felt pieces under the wrong side of the green, purple, and blue fabric. Place the green corduroy right sides together with the green, purple, and blue fabric. Machine stitch all the way around the edge, ½ inch (1.3 cm) in from the edge. Leave a 3-inch (7.6 cm) opening on one edge. Clip the corners.

4 Turn the piece right sides out. Push out the corners with the knitting needle. Press. Press the open section folded in. Hand stitch closed. Machine topstitch all around the edge ½ inch (1.3 cm) in from the edge.

5 Place the 5½ x 7-inch (14 x 17.8 cm) pieces of corduroy right sides together. (You will have a 4½ x 6-inch [11.4 x 15.2 cm] piece after sewing.) Machine stitch all around the edge ½ inch (1.3 cm) in, and leave a 3-inch (7.6 cm) opening on one edge. Clip the corners.

6 Turn the piece right sides out, and push out the corners with the knitting needle. Press with the opening folded to the inside. Hand stitch closed.

7 Following the manufacturer's instructions for the iron-on adhesive, place the adhesive on the back of the three floral prints. Draw the flower designs on the paper backing of the adhesive, and cut out the flowers.

8 Place the flowers on the corduroy, and pin them down (figure 1). Pin the ribbon and rickrack on so they look like stems. Remove the flowers. Zigzag the ribbon and rickrack in place using invisible thread in the needle and regular thread in the bobbin.

figure 1

9 Remove the paper backing from the flowers, and press in place on the corduroy piece. Zigzag, with invisible thread in the needle, around the whole edge of each flower, and make sure the needle hits the flower and the corduroy. Make the stitches close together.

10 Hand stitch the buttons and beads in position on the flowers. Embellish the flowers with embroidery floss. Use a straight stitch and French knots. Attach the corduroy piece, and use the blue embroidery thread with a blanket stitch all the way around the edge.

STICKY SITUATION

Because you're drawing on the paper backing of the iron-on adhesive, keep in mind the finished appliqué will be the reverse of any pattern you use.

pinning**zoo**

*S*oft, charming, and simple, these embroidered, line-drawn animals are a great addition to a basic sewing kit. Without pins, they'd make an adorable accent for a baby's nursery.

DESIGNER

CASSIE GRIFFIN

WHAT YOU NEED

Basic sewing tools

Muslin

Water soluble marker or pencil

Embroidery hoop

Embroidery floss, various colors

Twill tape, natural color

Sewing machine (optional)

Iron

WHAT YOU DO

1 Draw or trace one of the template designs (page 298), or a design of your own, for embroidering onto the muslin with a water-soluble marker or pencil. Make sure the design falls within a 4 x 6-inch area.

2 Using an embroidery hoop and embroidery needle, embroider the design using one or two colors of floss and a simple outline stitch, backstitch, or stem stitch.

3 Measure a 4 x 6-inch section of the muslin, centered on the embroidered work. Cut it out, and also cut one plain 4 x 6-inch piece of muslin for the back.

4 Fold the twill tape in half with its ends matching. Pin it to the right side of the back piece at the top center. Match the ends of the tape to the raw edges of the muslin. The loop will be sandwiched between the front and back pieces when you sew.

5 With right sides facing, pin the front and back pieces together, and sew all around with a ½-inch seam allowance. Leave a 1½-inch opening at the bottom for stuffing.

6 Before turning the fabric right side out, press back the unsewn seam on the seam line to make hand sewing easier later.

7 Turn the fabric right side out. Use the eraser end of a pencil, or another tool, to push out the corners. Press the fabric, keeping the unsewn seam folded inside.

8 Stuff the fabric firmly with polyester fiberfill. Use the eraser end of the pencil to move stuffing into the corners.

9 Hand sew the opening closed, following the pressed edge of the seam line.

GENTLE STUFFING

Stuff the pincushion firmly, but don't overstuff or the seams may buckle.

all buttoned up

The four napkin rings in this clever project are easy to make, and you can add your own personal touches by matching fabric and button … or go against the grain and make four different ones.

DESIGNER

ROXANNE BEAUVAIS

WHAT YOU NEED

Basic sewing tools

Pattern (page 302)

¼ yard (22.9 cm) of cotton fabric (one fat quarter)

10-inch (25.4 cm) square of medium-weight sew-in interfacing

3 spools of thread: one matching the color of the fabric, one contrasting color, and one matching the color of the buttons

Iron-on hook-and-loop tape

4 buttons, ¾ inch (1.9 cm) or smaller

WHAT YOU DO

1 Cut out eight pattern pieces from the cotton fabric and four from the interfacing.

2 Layer two fabric pieces, right sides together. Place one piece of interfacing on top. Sew around the shape, leaving the needle down when you rotate the fabric to create a smooth curve. Leave a 2-inch (5.1 cm) opening along a straight edge to turn the ring right side out.

3 Notch the seam allowance on both curves, and then turn the ring right side out. Use the blunt end of the pencil to push out the curves. Press well.

4 Using the contrasting thread, topstitch around the entire ring ¼ inch (6 mm) from the edge. This will also close the 2-inch (5.1 cm) opening.

5 Fold the ring in half length-wise and mark the center. Starting at this center point, sew straight lines the long way, ¼ inch (6 mm) apart, to create a modern quilted pattern (see the photo below). Pull the threads through to one side, tie a knot, and clip the threads.

6 Iron on a 1-inch (2.5 cm) square of hook-and-loop tape in the position marked on the pattern. Apply the loop side to the bottom and the hook side to the top.

7 Hand sew a button on the top right-hand side of the cuff, opposite the hook-and-loop tape so that when closed, the button sits on the outside over the hook-and-loop tape.

8 Repeat steps 2 through 7 for additional rings.

*salsa*softies

DESIGNER

NATHALIE MORNU

$\mathcal{G}$et your groove on in the kitchen with these terry cloth potholders that can also clean any spills. For added spice, make your own bias tape for the perfect decorative finish. It only takes a few minutes of effort and adds lots of zest to the finished product.

WHAT YOU NEED

Basic sewing tools

1/3 yard (30.5 cm) of fabric for bias tape

1 patterned terry cloth towel

WHAT YOU DO

1 To make enough bias tape for both potholders, cut four strips of fabric 2 inches (5.1 cm) wide, and sew them together sequentially to make one long strip. Iron them in half, and then in half again, as described on page 20. Set aside.

2 Cut two circles, each 8 inches (20.3 cm) in diameter, out of the towel.

3 Stack the circles together, matching all edges. Pin them, then stitch all around, 1/4 inch (0.6 cm) from the edge. Trim a scant 1/8 inch (0.3 cm) all around.

4 Pin the bias tape all around the edge of one side of the stacked circles, lapping the ends with one turned under. Stitch. Flip the tape to the other side, and hand stitch it down, using slipstitch.

5 To make the matching square potholder, enlarge and cut out the template on page 299. Use this as a pattern to cut two square pieces out of the towel, and repeat steps 3 and 4 with this pair.

VERY TERRY

Two stacked layers of toweling are thick enough that you don't need to insert insulating material between them.

ribbon rounds

Keep this polka-dotted bolster as is, or untie the ribbon closure to fold it out into a cushion. A comfortable solution to game night or take-out dinner picnic on the living room floor!

WHAT YOU NEED

Basic sewing tools

16 x 36-inch (40.6 x 91.4 cm) piece of ½-inch (1.3 cm) foam

⅛ yard (11.4 cm) each of dark blue, green, and light blue faux suede

24 x 40-inch (61 x 101.6 cm) piece of ½-inch (1.3 cm) upholstery batting

½ yard (45.7 cm) of blue polka dot cotton fabric

3½ yards (3.2 m) of 1-inch (2.5 cm) blue patterned ribbon

Thread, white and blue

Embroidery floss, light and dark blue

Embroidery needle

SEAM ALLOWANCE

½ inch (1.3 cm) unless otherwise noted

FINISHED SIZE

12 x 6½ inches (30.5 x 16.5 cm)

DESIGNER

JOAN K. MORRIS

What You Cut

Foam
- *4 pieces, each 8 x 11 inches (20.3 x 27.9 cm)*

Upholstery Batting
- *4 pieces, each 10 x 11 inches (25.4 x 27.9 cm)*
- *4 pieces, each 6 x 11 inches (15.2 x 27.9 cm)*
- *8 pieces, each 4 x 4 inches (10.2 x 10.2 cm)*

Polka Dot Fabric
- *4 pieces, each 11 x 13 inches (27.9 x 33 cm)*

WHAT YOU DO

1 Enlarge the template on page 300, and copy it. Use it as a pattern to cut two circles each from the green and the light blue fabrics. Cut four circles from the dark blue. Cut the fabric as described in the box, above.

2 Make the tube forms. Center one of the pieces of foam on one of the 6 x 11-inch (15.2 x 27.9 cm) pieces of batting. Roll the foam lengthwise, with batting on the outside, into a tube. Hold the shape while you pin.

Use long straight pins and push them down through the layers. Hand-baste using the white thread. Tuck one batting square into each end to close the ends and baste. Repeat until you have four forms.

3 Make the tube covers. Fold the cut pieces of polka dot fabric in half lengthwise with right sides together. On all covers, machine-stitch 4 inches (10.2 cm) in from each end. Do not turn.

4 Sew a matching pair of circles to the ends of each tube cover. Slightly hand gather the circles as you sew to ease them into the seams for a perfect fit. Notch the curves, and turn.

5 Insert a form into one tube cover through the long opening. Turn the seam allowance under, and use the light blue embroidery floss to blanket-stitch across the entire length of the seam. Use dark blue embroidery floss to blanket-stitch around the circles at their seams. Repeat for all tubes.

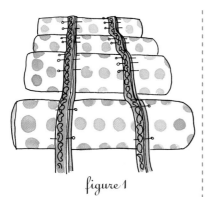

figure 1

6 Assemble the pillows by first laying the tubes parallel in front of you. Alternate the tubes by the color of their end circles. Position the tubes so the two at the center touch. Move the two outer tubes 2 inches (5.1 cm) away from the center tubes (figure 1).

7 Cut the ribbon in half and lay each piece across the tubes, 3 inches (7.6 cm) in from the ends, and pin in place. Hand-stitch the ribbon to the tubes using blue sewing thread.

8 Starting where you attached the ribbon to the first tube, blanket-stitch down one side of the ribbon, across the ribbon and down the other side. Do the same for the other ribbon. Do not blanket-stitch the edges of the unattached ribbon, which will become the ties.

9 Roll up the tubes and tie the ribbons in bows. Or, lay the tubes flat and tie bows on each end.

scorchin'!

Some like it hot, but your hands will thank you for making this protective, heat-resistant oven mitt. Batting material or terry cloth fabric provide the necessary insulation to keep you feeling cool.

DESIGNER

AIMEE RAY

WHAT YOU NEED

Basic sewing tools

Red patterned fabric, about 15 x 12 inches (38.1 x 30.5 cm)

White cotton fabric, about 15 x 24 inches (38.1 x 61 cm)

Terry cloth or quilt batting, 15 x 16 inches (38.1 x 40.6 cm)

Embroidery floss in different colors

Embroidery needle and hoop

WHAT YOU DO

1 Enlarge the pattern on page 299 and cut it out. Cut one piece of the red fabric for the back, and cut three pieces of the white fabric—one for the front and two for the lining. Cut two

more mitt-shaped pieces ½ inch (1.3 cm) smaller than the pattern out of the insulation material.

2 Transfer the flame designs onto one of the white pieces of fabric. Cut a "cuff" from the red fabric to fit the opening, making it with a slightly curved edge. Iron the curved edge under ¼ inch (0.6 cm). Pin it in place at the bottom of the white piece, and stitch it on using the appliqué stitch. Select a word you like (see tip box); embroider it and the flames using split stitch.

3 To make the hanging strap, cut a 2 x 7-inch (5.1 x 17.8 cm) strip from the white fabric. Fold it lengthwise, right sides out, then lengthwise again with the edges inside. Sew along the edge.

4 Pin the embroidered piece to one of the linings, right sides facing and edges matching. Sew ¼ inch (0.6 cm) from the edge, leaving the straight edge open. Set aside. Repeat with the back piece and the remaining lining.

HOT STUFF

Maybe your potholder's not scorchin' or *caliente*... It could be *brûlant*, *n'est-ce pas?* Or *het*, if you're making Swedish meatballs. Serve pizza piping *caldo* from the oven for dinner, and eat the leftovers cold for breakfast. And apple strudel tastes best *heiß*.

5 Snip the fabric around the curves, and turn each piece right side out. Slide one of the insulating pieces inside each mitt section, and stitch up the openings with the hidden stitch.

6 Pin both halves of the mitt, right sides together, with edges matched. Pin the strap ends at the bottom corner to form a loop. Sew ¼ inch (0.6 cm) from the edges, leaving the straight edge open.

7 Snip the fabric around the curved edges, and turn the mitt right side out.

login

A geometric wonder, the log cabin design of this quilted potholder is anything but square.

DESIGNER

BETSY COUZINS

WHAT YOU NEED

Basic sewing tools

Scraps of a variety of all-cotton fabrics, totaling about ¼ yard (22.9 cm)

Piece of cotton fabric for the back, 9 inches (22.9 cm) square

Piece of low-loft quilt batting, 9 inches (22.9 cm) square

Rotary cutter

Self-healing cutting mat

SEAM ALLOWANCE

¼ inch (0.6 cm)

WHAT YOU DO

1 With the rotary cutter and ruler on the cutting mat, cut the fabrics into strips 1½ inches (3.8 cm) wide and of any length. Make sure some strips are at least 9 inches (22.9 cm) long.

2 Choose two strips for the center blocks. Cut one strip to make a 1½-inch (3.8 cm) square. Leave the other strip the original length. With the right sides together, pin and sew on one side of the square.

3 Trim the long strip even with the square (figure 1). Press the seam open, then to the side. Choose the next strip of fabric, and place it right-side up on the work surface.

4 Placing the right sides together, pin the sewn pieces on top of the new strip, with three edges lined up and the extra length of the new strip continuing off to the right (figure 2). Sew along the top edge, and trim the extra length off. Open the seam, and press it to the side. Turn the foundation piece—what you've already sewn together—90°, so the newest piece is on the left side when facing up.

5 Choose another fabric strip, put it right-side up on the work surface, and repeat step 4.

figure 1

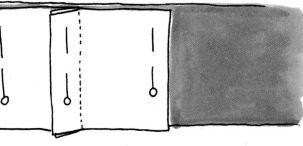

figure 2

189

Continue repeating until the foundation measures 8½ inches (21.6 cm) square. If necessary, trim it exactly square.

6 Place the backing fabric face down on the work surface, and cover it with the batting. Place the foundation face up on top of the batting, and pin all three layers together.

7 Starting at the first block you made, sew through the middle of the strips in a squared spiral, as shown in figure 3. When you get to the end, sew all the way to the edge and backstitch. Trim off the excess batting and backing fabric.

8 Cut four strips from the same fabric, each 1½ x 9½ inches (3.8 x 24.1 cm), and use them to bind the edges of the potholder.

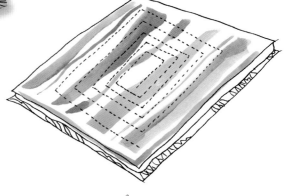

figure 3

TINT HINT

Choosing fabrics in two colorways—yellow-orange and green-blue, for example—will give some structure to the log cabin pattern.

190

cute+curious

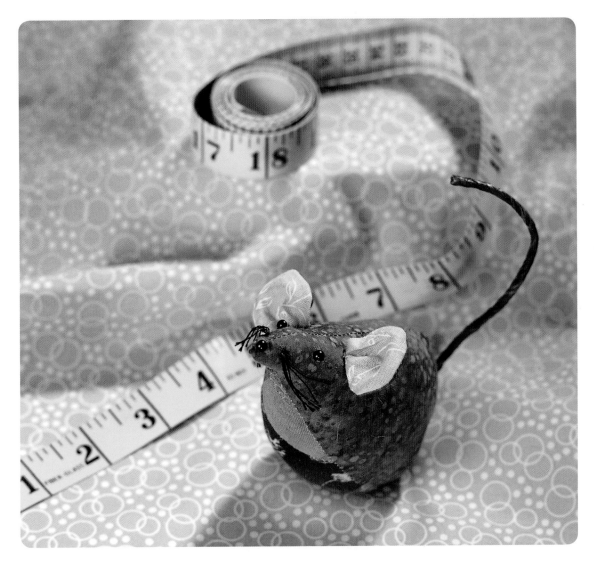

*W*atch the cat when this little creature is out. Cuter than the real thing, he stays upright with a small river rock sewn inside for a base.

DESIGNER

CASSIE GRIFFIN

WHAT YOU NEED

Basic sewing tools

Assorted fabrics scraps, browns and pink

Sewing machine (optional)

Knitting needle

1-inch, flat, round river rock

Hot glue and glue gun

6-inch wood-covered wire

Embroidery floss, black

3 black seed beads

½"

WHAT YOU DO

1 Make a pattern from the template (page 300) for the mouse.

2 Piece together strips of pink and brown fabrics, sewing the strips with narrow seams, and pressing them open. Cut one chest out of the pieced fabric. Cut two body pieces from brown fabric, and cut two ears from brown and two ears from pink fabric.

3 With right sides together, machine stitch (or hand sew) the body pieces with a ¼-inch seam allowance. Sew from the tail area, up the back, and over the nose ½ inch, creating the point of the nose (see above).

4 Machine stitch or hand sew the chest piece in place, leaving an opening at the bottom large enough to fit the river rock. Clip curves in the seam allowance and turn the mouse right side out. Push out the points carefully with a knitting needle.

5 Stuff the body firmly with polyester fiberfill, a little at a time, starting at the nose. Use the knitting needle to push the stuffing into the nose point.

6 Insert the rock into the bottom of the body, and position it for the mouse to stand upright. Hot glue the rock in place.

7 Position the wood-covered wire for the tail, bend it into the desired curl, and glue it in place with hot glue. Then, close the hole at the bottom, hand stitching over the rock and the wire.

8 Place the brown and pink ear pieces with right sides together and stitch them, leaving an opening for turning. Turn them right side out, and hand stitch them in place on the mouse.

9 Hand stitch the seed beads in position for the eyes and the nose. Stitch black embroidery floss through the snout for the whiskers. Place a dot of fabric glue at the base of the whiskers to keep them in position, and separate the strands.

dot's diner

$\mathcal{W}$ho doesn't love polka dots? Even better, you can slip your hand in the secret pocket and hold a steaming hot dish in safe, sassy style.

DESIGNER

WENDI GRATZ

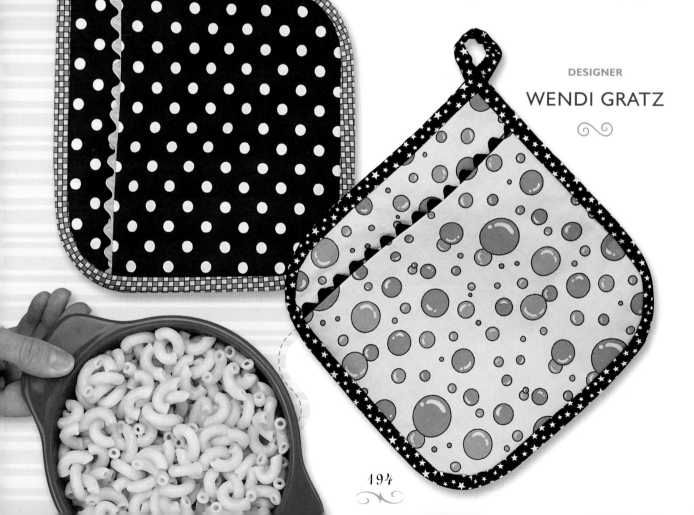

WHAT YOU NEED

Basic sewing tools

1/4 yard (22.9 cm) of fabric

1/8 yard (11.4 cm) of fabric for bias tape

1/4 yard (22.9 cm) of cotton batting

8 inches (20.3 cm) of rickrack 1/2 inch (1.3 cm) wide

SEAM ALLOWANCE

1/4 inch (0.6 cm)

WHAT YOU DO

1 Copy the templates on page 301. Cut two pieces of fabric from each pattern piece, and cut one piece of batting using the larger pattern piece, which serves as the front and back of the potholder.

2 Pin the rickrack to the front of one of the pockets (the smaller fabric pieces), 1/2 inch (1.3 cm) from the edge of the straight side and stitch.

3 Pin the pocket pieces right sides together. Sew on the stitching line created in step 2 with the rickrack embedded between. Open the seam and press. The rickrack should peek up from the seam.

4 Put the front piece face down on your work surface. Place the batting over it and then the back piece, face up. Finally, put the pocket on top, matching all the curved edges. Pin the layers together.

5 Make a strip of bias tape 2 1/4 inches (5.7 cm) wide and 40 inches (101.6 cm) long (see page 20). Fold it in half the long way and press.

6 Starting from the square corner, pin the bias tape along the edge of the potholder with the raw edges together. Stitch slowly around the curves to ease the fabric in, and when you get back to the corner where you started, stop the machine, and leave the potholder where it is. Turn under the binding at the beginning to the back of the potholder, and continue stitching about 4 inches (10.2 cm) past the edge of the potholder. Remove the potholder from the sewing machine.

7 Turn the binding to the back of the potholder. Hand stitch the folded edge of the binding to the back of the potholder. Stitch the extra tail of binding to itself so the raw edges are enclosed. Turn the tail into a hanging loop, and stitch the end securely to the potholder.

TRIM AND TIDY

As you sew, guide the raw edge of the fabric along the 1/2-inch (1.3 cm) mark on the throat plate of the machine so the rickrack passes under the needle. This will prevent the trim from shifting between the layers of fabric later and gives you a sewing line so the rickrack is perfectly embedded in the seam.

new neutral

A strategically off-center focal point, delicate surface detailing, and a thoroughly modern aesthetic make this quilted work of art an elegant accent to any room. Trés chic!

DESIGNER

MALKA DUBRAWSKY

WHAT YOU NEED

Basic sewing tools

7 fabric scraps of print cotton in pale shades and white, none less than 4 x 10 inches (10.2 x 25.4 cm)

¼ yard (22.8 cm) of bleached cotton

¼ yard (22.8 cm) of unbleached cotton muslin

½ yard (45.7 cm) of print cotton for the pillow back

⅛ yard (11.4 cm) of print cotton for the binding

18-inch (45.7 cm) square of cotton muslin for quilting

18-inch (45.7 cm) square of cotton batting

Safety pins

Darning foot

12-inch (30.5 cm) zipper

Zipper foot

12 x 12-inch (30.5 x 30.5 cm) pillow form

SEAM ALLOWANCE

¼ inch (6 mm) unless otherwise noted

FINISHED SIZE

13 x 13 inches (33 x 33 cm)

WHAT YOU DO

1 Copy and enlarge the template on page 290 and cut out the pieces.

2 Pin pieces 1–7 of the template to the seven different print cotton scraps and cut them out. Pin pieces 8, 12, 13, 14, and 17 to the bleached white cotton and cut. Pin pieces 9, 11, 15, and 16 to the unbleached cotton muslin and cut.

3 Cut two pieces, each 9 x 18 inches (22.9 x 45.7 cm), from the fabric for the pillow back. Cut the fabric for the binding on the diagonal into strips that are 1¼ inches (3.2 cm) wide.

4 Make the pillow top. Using the template as reference, sew piece 1 to piece 2 along the edge as noted, and press. Sew piece 3 to the two stitched pieces and press. Continue sewing the pieces of the pillow top in order, pressing them as you go.

5 Lay the 18-inch (45.7 cm) square of muslin on your work surface. Lay the 18-inch (45.7 cm) square of batting on top and the pieced top right side up on both layers of fabric. Pin with safety pins through all layers.

figure 1

6 With white thread, and using the darning foot on your sewing machine, quilt the layers. Use free-motion quilting to make a diamond pattern (figure 1). Remove the pins as you sew. Trim the edges of the layers flush.

7 On one of the long edges of one piece of fabric cut for the back, turn under ¼ inch (6 mm) and press. Turn under again 1½ inches (3.8 cm) and press. On one of the long edges of the other back piece, turn under ¼ inch (6 mm) and press. Stitch the zipper to the pressed edges.

8 Lay the quilted pillow front on the zippered back with wrong sides together and pin. Trim the pieces flush. Sew the front to the back around the edges.

9 Sew the strips for the binding together to make one long strip as you would for making bias tape.

10 Bind the edges and miter the corners following your favorite method. Before you begin sewing the binding to the raw edge, leave a 4-inch (10.2 cm) tail for overlapping. Once you turn the binding over the raw edge, use a zigzag stitch to hold it down.

11 Stuff the pillow with the form.

eco on-the-go

You'll find this pillow an indispensible travel companion. Just roll it up, and tuck it into its own compact carrying case. Made from organic cotton and stuffed with bamboo fiber, it's gentle on you and the planet.

WHAT YOU NEED

Basic sewing tools

¼ yard (22.8 cm) each of three complementary fabrics for fabric A, fabric B, and fabric C

Thread to match

12-ounce (340 g) bag of bamboo fiber for stuffing

30 inches (76.2 cm) of ½-inch (1.3 cm) vintage seam binding or ribbon

SEAM ALLOWANCE

½ inch (1.3 cm) unless otherwise noted

FINISHED SIZE

Pillow: 12 x 9 inches (30.5 x 22.9 cm)
Case: 10 x 5 inches (25.4 x 12.7 cm)

DESIGNER

VALERIE SHRADER

WHAT YOU DO

TRAVEL PILLOW

1 Cut a 10 x 13-inch (25.4 x 33 cm) piece each from fabric A and fabric B; one for the front of the pillow and one for the back. Note: This project uses an organic bamboo solid and two cotton prints. Since the bamboo fabric is cushier, it is used for the front of the pillow. From fabric C, cut two strips for the decorative flange, each 1½ x 24½ inches (3.8 x 62.2 cm).

2 To make the flange, stitch two short ends of the strips together with right sides facing to make one long strip. Press the seam open. Fold in one short end ½ inch (1.3 cm) and press. Fold the entire strip in half lengthwise with wrong sides facing, and press.

3 Starting with the unpressed short edge of the strip, pin the flange to the pillow front with right sides together and raw edges aligned. Stitch the flange to the pillow, beginning 1 inch (2.5 cm) from the end of the strip. Miter the corners as if you were binding a quilt. When you approach the end of the strip, overlap the ends. Fold the flange over the raw edges and sew down to finish.

4 Pin the front of the pillow to the back, right sides together, and stitch around the entire edge, leaving a 3-inch (7.6 cm) opening for turning and stuffing. Trim the corners and turn right side out.

5 Stuff the pillow to the desired firmness. Use a slipstitch to close the opening.

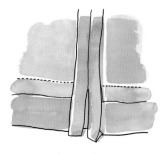

figure 1

STUFF SACK

6 Cut a patchwork panel for the sack as desired using fabrics A, B, and C with the final dimensions of the panel being 10 x 13 inches (25.4 x 33 cm). Cut a casing strip from one of the fabrics that is 3 x 13 inches (7.6 x 33 cm). Cut a circle for the bottom from one of the fabrics that is 5 inches (12.7 cm) in diameter.

7 Sew the patchwork panel. Note: For added strength, double-stitch each seam in the sack. Press under ½ inch (1.3 cm) on one long edge of the casing strip. Pin the other long raw edge to the top of the patchwork panel, right sides facing, and stitch.

8 Stitch the side seam of the panel together beginning at the casing seam. Do not stitch the side seams of the casing together (figure 1). Press the seam open, folding under the raw edges of the casing seam and pressing them under.

9 Mark the circular bottom and the sack at 90, 180, 270, and 360°. Match the marks and pin the bottom to the sack, clipping the seam allowance of the sack as necessary to ease the circular bottom in the seam.

10 Fold the casing strip to the inside and stitch in the ditch along the seam line, making sure to catch the folded edge in the seam. Thread the seam binding or ribbon through the casing. Stuff the pillow into the sack by rolling lengthwise.

RAID THAT STASH

If you're buying fabric, you'll need at least a ¼ yard (22.8 cm) of each fabric to get the length required for the pillow. However, you can just as easily use fabric scraps from your stash and cut them to the dimensions listed above.

corsagepins

Sewing
a big project is a snap with this
sunshiny wrist corsage. Fasten
it in place, and your pins won't
get buried under patterns and
prints as you work.

DESIGNER

CASSI GRIFFIN

WHAT YOU NEED

Basic sewing tools

Wool felt, green, three shades
of yellow

Embroidery floss, matching colors

Acetate or cardboard

Snap and snap tool, or hook and
loop tape

WHAT YOU DO

1 Create a pattern from the
template (page 298), and cut
the pincushion pieces from felt as
follows: Petal A, cut 10 in dark yellow; Petal B, cut eight in medium
yellow; Petal C, cut six in light
yellow; Petal D, cut five in dark
yellow; and Petal E, cut three in
medium yellow. Cut two of the
Pincushion piece from green, and
cut one of the plastic insert from
the acetate. Cut the band, wrist
strap, and tab from green.

2 Stitch the short sides of the
tab to the center of the pincushion back using running stitches
and two strands of green floss.

3 To make the wrist strap, apply one half of the snap to one strap. Apply the other half of the snap to the other strap. Place the straps with wrong sides together, with straps at opposite ends and on opposite sides. Blanket stitch the two wrist straps together using three strands of green floss and the embroidery needle. Set aside.

4 To create the pincushion top, overlap the Petal A pieces in a circle on the outer edge of the pincushion top piece. Position them to overhang the edge by half. Whipstitch each in place at its center using two strands of yellow floss.

5 Position each consecutive round of petals inside and overlapping the last set (see at right). Stitch each round in place in the same manner. Place the last round of petals directly on top of the previous round, alternating spacing, and stitch in place.

6 Using three strands of green floss, blanket stitch the side-band to the pincushion top. Tuck under each edge, and use small running stitches to secure the edges to the pincushion.

7 Stitch the pincushion bottom onto the other side of the pin-cushion band using three strands of green floss in a blanket stitch. At the halfway point, stop and place the plastic insert inside, on the bottom. Continue stitching. Leave a 1½-inch opening for stuffing.

8 Stuff firmly with polyester fiberfill between the top of the pincushion and the plastic insert. Then stitch the opening closed. Slide the strap through the tab on the back of the pincushion.

ACETATE ALTERNATIVE

If you don't have plastic acetate on hand for the plastic insert, use anything that will keep pins from poking through to your wrist—cut a disc from the plastic lid of a yogurt container, for example.

closeknitfriends

*P*reserve and repurpose the wool from a favorite sweater with these charming pincushions.

DESIGNER

JOAN K. MORRIS

WHAT YOU NEED

Basic sewing tools

Felted wool sweater or commercial felt

Sewing machine (optional)

Knitting needle

Embroidery floss, off-white

5 white buttons ($\frac{1}{4}$ inch)

18 inches thin coordinating ribbon

WHAT YOU DO

1 Make the pattern for the sweater using the template (page 301). Position the pattern at the bottom edge of the felted sweater, on the sweater hem or ribbing. Cut two pieces. Lay the pocket pattern at the neck edge of the sweater, and cut two pockets. Set the pockets aside.

2 Place the sweater pieces with right sides together and pin. Machine stitch or hand sew them with a $\frac{1}{4}$-inch seam allowance, leaving the bottom edge open. Turn the sweater right side out, using a knitting needle to help push out the corners.

3 Stuff the sweater firmly with bits of polyester fiberfill, filling the sleeves first and working your way back to the opening. Hand stitch the bottom closed using a whipstitch with matching thread.

4 Stitch the pockets in place using a blanket stitch with embroidery floss and an embroidery needle. Sew a blanket stitch around the neck, the bottom of the sleeves, and down the center front, a little off center. Stitch the buttons in place down the front.

5 Thread the large-eye embroidery needle with coordinating ribbon, and stitch it in place at the neck. Tie a small bow.

Turtleneck Variation

Create this pincushion the same way you did the sweater pincushion, but place the turtleneck pattern at the neck edge of the sweater. Slide the pattern down so the top rests just below the ribbing or hem of the neck of the wool sweater. Follow the dotted lines of the pattern to cut the turtleneck straight up, through the finished neck edge of the wool sweater. Sew the turtleneck the same as for the sweater pincushion, except sew the bottom closed and leave the neck end open for stuffing. Stitch on buttons at the neck, if desired. (Omit the pockets for the turtleneck variation.)

sweettreat

Finally, a dessert without all the calories! Whip up this tasty treat with sweet cupcake embroidery and a strawberries-and-cream color palette.

DESIGNER

AIMEE RAY

WHAT YOU NEED

Basic sewing tools

6 x 6-inch (15.2 x 15.2 cm) corner piece of pink patterned fabric

8½-inch (21.6 cm) square of white cotton fabric

6 x 2-inch (15.2 x 5.1 cm) strip of pink cotton fabric

8½-inch (21.6 cm) square of pink patterned fabric

Embroidery floss in dark pink, pink, brown, cream, red, green, and white

Embroidery needle and hoop

7½-inch (19 cm) square of quilt batting or terry cloth

WHAT YOU DO

1 Using the template on page 303 as a pattern, cut a corner piece from the pink fabric. Iron the curved edge under ¼ inch (0.6 cm). Pin it face up on the white square, matching corners, and appliqué it on.

2 Transfer the cupcake designs from page 303 onto the white square of fabric. Embroider them using split stitch and satin stitch. Embroider a scalloped design along the curved edge of the pink appliquéd fabric, and stitch a word you think describes dessert.

3 To make the hanging tab, fold the 6 x 2-inch (15.2 x 5.1 cm) strip of fabric lengthwise, right sides out, then lengthwise again with the edges inside. Sew along the edge.

4 Line up the embroidered square with the pink square, right sides facing, and pin them together. Place the hanging tab at the corner, and pin between both pieces of material. Fold to form a loop that rests on the fabric.

5 Sew around the edges using a ½-inch (1.3 cm) seam allowance. Leave 3 to 4 inches (7.6 to 10.2 cm) open.

6 Snip the fabric at the corners, and turn the potholder right side out. Slip the batting or terry cloth square inside, and smooth it flat.

7 Embroider a running stitch all around the potholder, ½ inch (1.3 cm) from the edge and through all the layers, hiding the knot in the floss on the inside of the potholder.

8 Sew up the opening using a hidden stitch.

FEELING LOOPY

To make sure a hanging tab sewn into a seam has the proper orientation after you turn the potholder right side out, just remember this: match the raw edges of the potholder and of the strip.

belt it out

$\mathcal{D}$o you want to get the belt? Well, then stop what you're doing and make one! With groovy cotton prints and an adjustable loop, you'll be amazed how fun these are to make—and wear.

DESIGNER

ERIN HARRIS

WHAT YOU NEED

Basic sewing tools

Small amounts of 8 to 12 different cotton prints, each at least 2 x 4 inches (5.1 x 10.2 cm)

Thread

1/4 yard (22.9 cm) of 45-inch (1.14 m) wide heavy fusible interfacing

2 D-rings, each 1 1/2 inches (3.8 cm)

SEAM ALLOWANCE

Varies

WHAT YOU DO

1 Take your belt measurement around your waist or hips, and add 6 inches (15.2 cm) to the number to get what we'll call measurement Y. That gives you about a 5-inch (12.7 cm) overlap when you pass the belt through the D-rings.

2 With the rotary cutter and ruler, cut your fabric into 4-inch (10.2 cm) strips of various widths with no piece narrower than 2 inches (5.1 cm).

3 Lay out your fabric as you choose. Starting from the left, sew your strips right sides together along the 4-inch (10.2 cm) side using a 1/4-inch (0.6 cm) seam allowance. (This is also known as strip-piecing.) Keep piecing left to right until your strip is equal in length to your measurement Y. Press all seams open.

4 Cut a piece of the interfacing into a strip that is 3 inches high and 1 inch shorter than your meaurement Y from step 1. With the wrong side of the belt facing up, center the interfacing on the belt, fusible side down, and leave a 1/2-inch (1.3 cm) border on all sides.

5 Iron the interfacing onto your belt following the manufacturer's instructions. Fold in both short ends of the belt 1/2 inch (1.3 cm), and press in place. Fold the top and bottom of the belt down 1/2 inch (1.3 cm), and press in place.

6 Fold the belt in half and press. Pin in place. Starting at one end, sew your belt together by topstitching 1/8 inch (0.3 cm) from the open edge. At the corners, keep your needle in the down position, and pivot 90°. Continue until you have topstitched all four sides of the belt.

7 insert an inch (2.5 cm) of the belt through the D-rings, and fold it over. Topstitch two parallel lines about 1/4 inch (0.6 cm) apart to secure the D-rings. Backstitch at both ends of both lines to make sure the belt won't come apart.

pinpals

You'll love pushing your pins into these plump little succulents. Watch out that they don't poke back!

DESIGNER

TONI WEBER

∾

boycactus

WHAT YOU NEED

Basic sewing tools

Green fleece or wool

Sewing machine (optional)

2 small buttons

1 small bead

Embroidery floss, brown

WHAT YOU DO

1. Make a pattern for the boy on scrap paper from the template (page 305). Cut out two body pieces, one gusset, one bottom, and four arm pieces from the fleece.

2. Sew one arm by laying two arm pieces with wrong sides together and stitching them with a ¼-inch exposed seam. Repeat for the second arm. Pin the arms to the wrong side of one body piece, facing inward, positioned at different heights (like a cactus).

3. Pin the gusset to the same side of the body as the arms. Use pins liberally, and ease the fabric into the curve.

4. Sew a ¼-inch seam around the cactus. Clip the top curve of the seam allowance. Repeat, sewing the second body piece to the other side of the gusset.

5. Pin the bottom piece to the body. Sew with a ¼-inch seam allowance, leaving a gap in the seam for turning right side out.

6. Turn the body right side out, and stuff with polyester fiberfill about three-quarters full, giving the body a nice firm feel. Add ¼ cup of rice for bottom weight. Top off with more polyester fiberfill, and hand stitch the opening closed.

7. Use a pen to mark the placement for the eyes and nose. Sew on two small buttons for the eyes and a small bead for the nose. Embroider a simple mouth.

8. For the cactus spines, use a needle threaded with a long length of brown embroidery floss. Take the needle in and out at the top of the head, leaving a 2-inch tail of floss, and snipping off 2 inches on the other side. Continue in a random pattern across the head. Tie off and knot each spine, trimming as desired.

girl cactus

WHAT YOU NEED

Basic sewing tools

Green fleece or wool

Sewing machine (optional)

2 small buttons

1 small bead

Embroidery floss, brown

$\frac{5}{8}$-inch pink velvet ribbon

Fabric glue

WHAT YOU DO

1. Make a pattern for the girl cactus on scrap paper from the template (page 305). Cut out two body pieces, one gusset, and one bottom from the fleece.

2. Follow steps 3 through 7 for Boy Cactus, omitting the arms.

3. Cut a $10\frac{3}{4}$-inch length of ribbon, and sew a long running stitch down the center with matching embroidery floss.

CACTUS SOFT TOY

To make a soft toy rather than a pincushion, leave out the rice when stuffing. Then embroider the face onto the cactus instead of using buttons, which could create a choking hazard for children.

REPURPOSING WOOL

Scavenge material from an old fleece or wool blanket, or pick one up at a thrift store for the material for this project.

4. Cinch the ribbon into little folds along the floss for a blossom. Keeping the blossom pinched together, tie a knot in the floss at the bottom of the blossom to secure it.

5. Stitch the blossom to the side of the head with one of the loose ends of floss. Knot and snip the excess floss. Add a drop of fabric glue beneath each side of the blossom for extra hold.

whipstitchitgood

*W*hip up this cupcake-shaped pincushion from scratch with a dash of scrap fabric, colorful stitching, and a few sweet buttons for a garnish.

DESIGNER

MEG ROOKS

WHAT YOU NEED

Basic sewing tools

Wool felt, 2 colors (see Felting, online)

Vintage fabric

Embroidery floss

Vintage buttons (large and small)

Vintage trim, 1 inch wide

WHAT YOU DO

1. Cut two 3½-inch diameter circles from wool felt, one 2-inch circle of vintage fabric, and one 1-inch circle of coordinating wool felt.

2. Using embroidery floss, carefully hand stitch the 2-inch fabric circle to the center of one large felt circle with stitches side by side.

3. Using a wider stitch, hand sew the 1-inch felt circle on top of the vintage fabric. Then, sew the buttons in a stack on top.

4. Whipstitch the trim to the top felt circle. Sew the ends of the trim together, tucking under the raw edge. Then, whipstitch the bottom felt circle to the trim, leaving a 2-inch opening for stuffing.

5. Add the stuffing, filling with a layer of rice, a layer of polyester fiberfill, and another layer of rice. Pack it tightly, and whipstitch to close the gap.

trupunto trio

Why stop at one? Triple your pleasure by making a terrific trio
of trupunto pillows. Once you master the easy technique for
this pillow you'll want to try it again (and again!).
Hint: Stuffing the quilt batting with fiberfill adds the extra loft.

DESIGNER

AMANDA CARESTIO

WHAT YOU NEED

Basic sewing tools

1 fat quarter of fabric A, a cotton solid in a light color

1 fat quarter of fabric B, a cotton print

¼ yard (22.8 cm) of fabric C, a cotton solid in a dark color

Polyester quilt batting

Thread to mach

Polyester fiberfill

SEAM ALLOWANCE

¼ inch (6 mm) unless otherwise noted

FINISHED SIZE

10½ x 9 inches (26.7 x 22.9 cm)

What You Cut

Fabric A
- 1 strip, 2¼ x 6 inches *(5.7 x 15.2 cm)*
- 1 rectangle, 4½ x 6 inches *(11.4 x 15.2 cm)*

Fabric B
- 2 rectangles, each 3 x 9 inches *(7.6 x 22.9 cm)*

Fabric C
- 1 strip, 1½ x 6 inches *(3.8 x 15.2 cm)*
- 1 square, 9½ inches (24.1 cm) square for the back
- 1 rectangle, 4½ x 9½ inches *(11.4 x 24.1 cm) for the back*

Quilt Batting
- 1 piece, 9 x 10½ inches *(22.9 x 26.7 cm)*

WHAT YOU DO

1 With right sides together, pin the strip cut from fabric C between the two pieces of fabric A along their 6-inch (15.2 cm) sides. Sew, and then press the seam allowances toward fabric C.

2 With right sides together, stitch the rectangles cut from fabric B to either side of the piece stitched in step 1. Press the seam allowances toward fabric B.

3 Lay the pillow front right side up on the piece of batting. Center the fabric on the batting and pin in place.

4 Using a thread that coordinates with fabric C, topstitch on fabric B ⅛ inch (3 mm) in from the seams.

EASY AS CAN BE

Coordinating a trio of complementary fabrics is easy when you remember a simple rule of three: (1) start with a print or plaid with at least three colors in it; (2) match the light color in the print to a light solid fabric; (3) do the same when choosing a dark solid. It works every time!

5 On fabric A, measure 1 inch (2.5 cm) up from its seam with fabric C. Stitch a horizontal line through both layers that runs across fabric A and between the two pieces of fabric B. From that line of stitching, measure up another 1 inch (2.5 cm) and stitch a line. Continue in this way until you reach the edge of the fabric. You should have a ¼-inch (6 mm) seam allowance left. Do the same, measuring and sewing, from the bottom seam of fabric C.

6 Turn the pillow front over to expose the batting. At the center of each sewn segment, cut one long slit in the batting that runs parallel to the lines of stitching. Make sure you cut only the batting and not the fabric of the pillow front.

7 For the pillow back, hem one edge on the square cut from fabric C. Fold and press the edge under ¼ inch (6 mm). Then fold under again, press, and sew. Pin the hemmed square to the pillow front, right sides facing, before pinning the unhemmed, Fabric C, rectangle. Stitch the sides. Do not turn.

8 Stuff the batting for the trapunto effect. Push the polyester fiberfill into the slits you cut in step 6. Fill them to nicely round each segment. Hand-stitch the slits closed.

9 Turn the pillow right side out and stuff with fiberfill. Pin the back opening together, then hand-stitch it closed using a slipstitch.

10 To round out your trio of pillows, mix and match fabrics by cutting strips and rectangles in different sizes to vary the look of the pieced pillow front. Always remember the batting layer so you can slit and stuff it later.

spot on

*I*f you're the type who just can't decide on one fabric, you'll enjoy this project that puts a happy dozen in the spotlight. Circular designs, spiraling surface stitches, and an easy grid pattern bring everything together.

DESIGNER

MALKA DUBRAWSKY

WHAT YOU NEED

Basic sewing tools

12 fabric scraps of print cotton, none less than 4 inches (10.2 cm) square

⅜ yard (34.3 cm) of print cotton for the pillow back

4-inch (10.2 cm) fabric squares for the appliqués: 5 of unbleached muslin, 4 of bleached cotton, 2 in ecru cotton, 1 in pale blue cotton

14-inch (35.6 cm) square of muslin for quilting

14-inch (35.6) square of cotton batting

2 strips of print cotton, 1¼ x 28 inches (3.2 x 71.1 cm) for the binding

2 pieces of muslin, each 9½ x 12½ inches (24.1 x 31.8 cm) for the pillow form

Safety pins

12-inch (30.5 cm) zipper

Darning foot

Zipper foot

Polyester fiberfill

SEAM ALLOWANCE

¼ inch (6 mm) unless otherwise noted

FINISHED SIZE

13 x 10 inches (33 x 25.4 cm)

WHAT YOU DO

1 Copy the template on page 303 and cut it out. Use it to trace 12 circles, one on each of the different fabric scraps. Cut them out. Cut two pieces for the pillow back from the print cotton, each 14 x 12 inches (35.6 x 30.5 cm) and set aside.

2 Machine-stitch ¼ inch (6 mm) in from the edge around each circle cut in step 1. Clip the seam, spacing the cuts approximately ¼ inch (6 mm) apart. Be careful to avoid cutting the stitching. On the wrong side, press the clipped edge toward the middle of the circle (figure 1).

figure 1

3 Center, and then pin a circle right side up on each of the 4-inch (10.2 cm) fabric squares. Edgestitch each circle to its square.

4 Arrange the squares in a pleasing manner to make a rectangle with three squares down and four across. Pin the first line of three squares to each other making a strip. Sew, and press the seams either to the right or left. Repeat to make another strip. Pin and sew the two strips together along their long edges and press.

5 Repeat step 4 to make another set of sewn strips. Sew the two sets together to complete the pieced top.

6 Lay the 14-inch (35.6 cm) square of muslin on your work surface. Lay the 14-inch (35.6 cm) square of batting on top of it. Lay the pieced top right side up on both layers of fabric and pin with safety pins thorough all layers.

7 With white thread, and using the darning foot on your sewing machine, sew through all layers to quilt. Use free-motion quilting to make concentric circles on each of the appliquéd circles. Trim the edges of the layers flush.

8 On one of the long edges of one piece of fabric cut for the back, turn under ¼ inch (6 mm) and press. Turn under again 1½ inches (3.8 cm) and press. On one of the long edges of the other back piece, turn under ¼ inch (6 mm) and press. Stitch the zipper to the pressed edges.

9 Sew the strips for the binding together to make one long strip as for making bias tape.

10 Bind the edges and miter the corners using your favorite method as you stitch the front to the back with wrong sides facing. Before you begin sewing the binding to the raw edge, leave a 4-inch (10.2 cm) tail for overlapping. Once you turn the binding over the raw edge, use a zigzag stitch to hold it down.

11 Using the two pieces of muslin, make a pillow form by stitching together with the right sides facing. Leave an opening to turn and stuff; stitch closed. Insert the form into the pillow.

WHY CUT?

Save time by using the precut squares of cotton favored by quilters. They're sold in blocks and grouped by fabric type and/or colorways. But be careful. They're so cute you may be tempted to buy way more than you need.

hold

card cache 222

just in case 224

bling sling 226

wooly tote 230

crafty carrier 233

eco chic 236

clutch me tightly 238

yoga to go 241

zippin' along 244

button clutchin' 246

you rang 249

tokyo rose 252

happy village 254

diaper snug 256

beach baby 259

yo, chica 262

rapper wrapper 265

snap attack 268

in the bag 271

sweet stash 274

we all scream 276

handy hook holder 278

dream on 281

under cover 284

card cache

These days, who bothers with cash? All you really need when you leave the house is I.D., keys, and a debit card. This pretty little case carries the bare essentials.

DESIGNER

JULIE ROMINE

WHAT YOU NEED

Basic sewing tools

Scraps of coordinating cotton fabric

Fusible lightweight interfacing

Key ring

Hook-and-loop tape

One ¾-inch (1.9 cm) button

Carabiner

SEAM ALLOWANCE

¼ inch (6 mm) unless otherwise noted

WHAT YOU DO

1 Enlarge the template on page 302. Cut two rectangles from different fabrics for the cozy body and one rectangle from the interfacing. Cut four tab pieces.

2 For the closure tab: With right sides together, stitch the tab on three sides. Trim the seam allowance to ⅛ inch (3 mm), clip the corners, and turn right side out. Fold in the raw ends ½ inch (1.3 cm) and press the tab. Set aside.

3 For the key ring tab: With right sides together, stitch the tab on two sides. Trim the seam allowance to ⅛ inch (3 mm) and turn right side out. Fold in half lengthwise, slip the key ring into the fold, and press. Set aside.

4 Pin the body rectangles right sides together. Lay the interfacing on top with the fusible side facing down. Lightly mark where the tab will be placed—when you stitch on all sides, leave an opening there (wider than the tab) for turning. Trim the interfacing close to the stitch line to reduce bulk, clip the corners, turn right side out, and press flat.

5 Tuck in the seam allowance at the opening and pin the ends of the key ring tab in the opening. Baste in place with a ⅛- inch (3 mm) seam allowance.

6 Fold the body piece in half with the fabric you want showing on the outside. Press to make a crease. Fold the short sides to create the card slots and press. Open up the body piece and lay it flat with the outside fabric facing up. Using the crease lines as a guide, place the closure

tab and hook-and-loop tape according to the template and stitch them in place (figure 1). Use a boxstitch (as shown) to secure the tab.

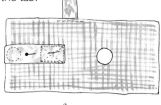

figure 1

7 Refold the side flaps and pin. Stitch them in place by running a ⅛ inch (3 mm) seam all the way down on both sides.

8 Sew hook-and-loop tape on the inside of the closure tab, checking that it aligns with the other half of the tape. Hand sew a button on the outside of the closure tab to hide the stitches for the hook-and-loop tape. Attach a carabiner to the key chain and you're all set to go shopping.

just in case

*T*he possibilities for this charming little case are endless. Stash your glasses, makeup, office supplies, digital camera, checkbooks, change, passport, or anything else that needs a good home.

DESIGNER

AUTUM HALL

WHAT YOU NEED

Basic sewing tools

¼ yard (22.9 cm) of linen fabric

¼ yard (22.9 cm) of cotton print for lining

6 scraps of cotton prints, 3 x 2 inches (7.6 x 5.1 cm), for patchwork

Fusible fleece

Heavyweight fusible interfacing

10-inch (25.4 cm) zipper

Thread

Fusible tape (optional)

SEAM ALLOWANCE

½ inch (1.3 cm) unless otherwise noted

WHAT YOU DO

1 Cut the fabric as described in the box at right. Arrange the 3 x 2-inch patchwork pieces in order for sewing. Join the 3-inch (7.6 cm) sides with a ¼-inch (6 mm) seam allowance. Press the seams, and trim the strip to 6 inches (15.2 cm). Sew the patchwork insert to the purse front right and left pieces, right sides together.

What You Cut

Linen
- 1 piece for the purse back, 6 x 10 inches (15.2 x 25.4 cm)
- 1 piece for the purse front left, 6 x 3 inches (15.2 x 7.6 cm)
- 1 piece for the purse front right, 6 x 5 inches (15.2 x 12.7 cm)

Cotton print
- 2 pieces for the lining, 6 x 10 inches (15.2 x 25.4 cm)

Fusible fleece
- 2 pieces, 6 x 10 inches (15.2 x 25.4 cm)

Fusible interfacing
- 2 pieces, 6 x 10 inches (15.2 x 25.4 cm)

Cotton print scraps
- Cut the 3-inch (7.6 cm) strips into various widths, up to 2 inches (5.1 cm), for the patchwork insert

2 Fuse the fleece to the wrong side of the purse front and purse back pieces. Fuse the interfacing to the wrong side of the cotton print lining pieces.

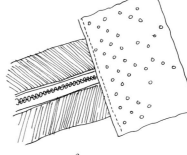

figure 1

3 Make tabs for the ends of the zipper with two scraps of fabric that are 2 inches (5.1 cm) long and the width of the zipper tape. Fold in half to 1 inch (2.5 cm) long and press. Place one tab on one end of the zipper with raw edges together (figure 1). Repeat with the other tab.

4 Install the zipper and lining using your favorite method. Stitch the sides and bottom, right sides facing.

SLICK ZIPPER TRICK

If pins make installing a zipper awkward, fuse a piece of fusible tape to both outside edges of the zipper tape instead. Then fuse the zipper to the purse back and the purse front instead of basting. Sew the zipper in place without pins!

bling sling

DESIGNER

VALERIE SHRADER

*K*eep your treasures safe on the road with this
well-designed jewelry pouch. The ring roll stays secure with a snap,
and there are two stash pockets—one with a zipper—inside.

WHAT YOU NEED

Basic sewing tools

3 fat quarters of different,
complementary fabric (A for
outside and zippered pocket;
B for lining, ties, and ring roll;
C for pocket and piping)

Matching thread

9-inch (22.9 cm) zipper in a
complementary color

6 inches (15.2 cm) of ⅜-inch
(9 mm) cording

Large hand sewing needle

Heavy-duty thread

Narrow tape

12-inch (30.5 cm) square of
craft felt

1 snap fastener

SEAM ALLOWANCE

½ inch (1.3 cm) unless otherwise
noted

What You Cut

Fabric A
- *1 piece for the outside, 6 x 10
  inches (15.2 x 25.4 cm)*
- *1 piece for the zippered
  pocket, 6 x 7 inches
  (15.2 x 17.8 cm)*

Fabric B
- *1 piece for the lining, 6 x 10
  inches (15.2 x 25.4 cm)*
- *2 strips, each 1 x 20 inches
  (2.5 x 50.8 cm), for the ties*
- *1 strip for the ring roll, 2 x 8
  inches (5.1 x 20.3 cm)*

Fabric C
- *1 piece for the pocket, 6 x 7
  inches (15.2 x 17.8 cm)*
- *2 strips, each 1½ x 10 inches
  (3.8 x 25.4 cm), for the
  piping*
- *Craft felt*
- *1 piece for the batting, 6 x 10
  inches (15.2 x 25.4 cm)*

WHAT YOU DO

1 Cut the fabric as described
in the box at left. Install the
zipper in the 6 x 7-inch (15.2
x 17.8 cm) piece of fabric A by
pressing under ¼ inch (6 mm)
on each of the 6-inch (15.2 cm)
edges. Center the zipper under
the edges, unzip the zipper, and
stitch the edges using a zipper
foot (figure 1). Make the pocket
by folding the fabric behind the
zipper tape, forming a flat tube.

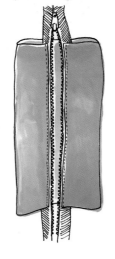

figure 1

2 Use the 6 x 7-inch (15.2 x 17.8 cm) piece of fabric B to make a pocket by folding lengthwise, right sides together, and stitch. Turn right side out and press.

3 Take the lining piece and pin the fabric A zippered pocket and the fabric B pocket in place. Stitch the bottom of the fabric B pocket in place, and stitch the top edge of the fabric A zippered pocket in place. Slide the zipper pull into the center of the pocket. Baste each pocket in place along the edges (figure 2).

figure 2

TOTIN' TREASURE

Pieced cotton prints are pretty, but if you own jewelry worthy of an heiress, try using silks or velvets instead!

4 To make the ring roll, wrap the 2 x 8-inch (5.1 x 20.3 cm) fabric B strip around the cording, right sides together. Using the zipper foot, stitch along the cording. Slide the fabric off the cording and stitch across one end. Turn it right side out. Place a narrow piece of tape around one end of the cording. Thread the needle and tie a knot in the end of a short, doubled strand of heavy-duty thread. Stitch through the taped end of the cording. Slide the needle through the roll and out the stitched end, pulling the cording through the roll. Clip the thread and needle as close to the sewn end as possible. Trim the roll to fit inside the side seam allowances of the pouch. Trim away ½ inch (1.3 cm) from the cording inside the open end of the roll and

place this end on the seam line at the right side of the lining. Sew a snap to the sewn end of the roll, placing the socket end on the lining and the ball end on the roll.

5 Make flat piping from the 1½ x 10-inch (3.8 x 25.4 cm) fabric C strips by pressing each in half lengthwise, wrong sides together. Pin one strip to each long edge of the pouch lining, placing the felt piece on the wrong side of the lining. Baste the piping in place.

6 Make the ties by folding each 1 x 20-inch fabric (2.5 x 50.8 cm) B strip in half lengthwise, pressing, and

folding each edge into the crease. Press the folded edges in to the center crease and stitch, folding under each short end. Baste the ties to the center of the top edge of the lining, stacking them one atop the other.

7 Place the front and the lining together, right sides facing, and pin in place. Stitch, leaving an opening at the bottom edge. Trim the seams, clip the corners, and turn right side out. Slipstitch the opening.

woolytote

DESIGNER

ERIN HARRIS

*F*rom the office to a night out, this wooly tote will carry you in style. For added richness, it's lined in silk and features strips of varying patterns and textures.

WHAT YOU NEED

Basic sewing tools

¾ yard (68.6 cm) of muslin for foundation

½ yard (45.7 cm) patterned wool for bag top

½ yard (45.7 cm) solid wool for handles

½ yard (45.7 cm) douppioni silk for bag lining, same color as handle wool

Pieces of 10 to 12 different wools in complementary colors for bottom patchwork, 11 inches (27.9 cm) long and varied widths: 3½ to 1½ inches (8.9 to 3.8 cm)

Thread

SEAM ALLOWANCE

Varies

WHAT YOU DO

1 With the rotary cutter, mat, and ruler, cut the following:

• 2 rectangles 8 x 14 inches (20.3 x 35.6 cm) and 2 rectangles 11 x 15 inches (27.9 x 38.1 cm) from the muslin

• 2 rectangles 8 x 14 inches (20.3 x 35.6 cm) from the patterned wool for the top

• 2 rectangles 29½ x 4 inches (74.9 x 10.2 cm) from the solid wool for the handles

• 14 x 28-inch (35.6 x 71.1 cm) rectangle from the silk for the lining

• 15 strips of wool, each 11 inches (27.9 cm) long, in varied widths of 1½ to 3½ inches (3.8 x 8.9 cm)

2 Lay out the two rectangles of muslin on your work surface. They will be used as a foundation for the two lower sides of the bag. Arrange seven or eight of the 15 strips of wool vertically on each of the muslin pieces. Using the foundation-piecing method and a ¼-inch (0.6 cm) seam allowance, piece the two bottom sections of the bag by stitching the strips to the muslin foundation.

3 Press both bottom pieces flat. With your rotary cutter and ruler, square the pieces so they measure 14 x 10 inches (35.6 x 25.4 cm). You may need to restitch the side pieces in place.

4 Pin one of the patterned wool fabric rectangles right side up to each of the foundation pieces, matching edges. Sew in place ¼ inch (0.6 cm) from the left side edge. Press flat, and then sew in place ¼ inch (0.6 cm) from the right side edge. Measure your rectangles, and square to 14 x 8 inches (35.6 x 20.3 cm) if necessary.

5 Pin the top pieces to the bottom pieces, right sides together. Sew together using a ½-inch (1.3 cm) seam allowance. Press seams open.

6 Pin the front of the tote to the back of the tote, matching raw edges. Using a ½-inch (1.3 cm) seam allowance, stitch together along both sides and the bottom of the bag. Clip the bottom corners, and press seams open.

7 Fold the top edge of the bag ½ inch (1.3 cm) toward the inside (wrong side) of the tote and press. Fold another 1½ inches (3.8 cm) toward the inside and press. Turn the tote right side out.

8 To make the lining, match the short sides of the lining rectangle right sides together, and press the fold. This fold is the bottom of your lining. Pin in place along both sides of the lining. Sew the sides together using a ½-inch (1.3 cm) seam allowance.

9 Clip the bottom corners of the lining seam allowance at a 45° angle, and be careful not to clip the stitching. Press the side seams open.

10 Place the lining into the tote, and line up the side seams. Make sure the bottom of the lining is all the way at the bottom of the bag. Slip the top edge of the lining under the folded edge of the bag, and pin in place. Topstitch around the bag 1¼ inches (3.2 cm) from the folded edge.

11 Make the handles by folding short ends of each handle rectangle ½ inch (1.3 cm) toward the wrong side and press. Fold long ends in to meet at the center and press. Fold the strap in half. Press and pin in place. Stitch up both sides of the strap ⅛ inch (0.3 cm) from each side edge.

12 Pin the straps to the bag so the outer side edges are 3 inches (7.6 cm) from the tote's side seams, and the bottom edges are 1 inch (2.5 cm) from the tote's top. Sew in place with a square and an X.

crafty carrier

*T*his is the perfect accessory for crafters on the go.
Pockets galore hold brushes, needles or hooks, scissors,
and more. Roll it up, tie a knot, and hit the road.

DESIGNER

SARAH LALONE

WHAT YOU NEED

Basic sewing tools

$^1/_2$ yard (45.7 cm) of quilting-weight cotton (interior)

$^1/_2$ yard (45.7 cm) of complementary quilting-weight cotton (exterior)

$^1/_2$ yard (45.7 cm) of fusible fleece

WHAT YOU DO

1 Cut a 9 x 12-inch (22.9 x 30.5 cm) rectangle from both fabrics and the fusible fleece. From the exterior fabric, also cut two 1$^1/_2$ x 12-inch (3.8 x 30.5 cm) strips for the ties. From the interior fabric, cut one 5 x 12-inch (12.7 x 30.5 cm) rectangle for the interior pocket panel.

2 To make each tie, fold over one short end $^1/_4$ inch (6 mm) and press. Fold the strip in half lengthwise to make a crease. Fold each long edge into the center crease and press. Refold the center crease, press, and topstitch. Form a knot in the tie, close to the stitched end. Set aside.

3 Following the manufacturer's instructions, fuse the fleece rectangle to the wrong side of the exterior piece of fabric. Set aside.

4 To make the interior pocket panel, press under the top edge $^1/_4$ inch (6 mm), press under another $^1/_2$ inch (1.3 cm), and stitch. With both right sides facing up, position the pocket on the interior piece, aligning the bottom edges. Pin the pieces together on the sides. With a water-soluble fabric marker or chalk pencil, draw guidelines for sewing the slots (see box), and stitch. Baste very close to the outermost edges on both sides.

5 To put it all together, start with the interior piece, right side up. Pin the raw ends of both ties on the right side, just above the pocket as shown (figure 1). Lay the exterior piece on top, right side down, fleece facing up.

6 Stitch all the way around through all the layers, leaving a 3-inch (7.6 cm) opening along the top for turning.

7 Trim the corners and seam allowances, and turn the project right side out. Turn under the raw edges at the opening and edgestitch or hand sew the opening closed.

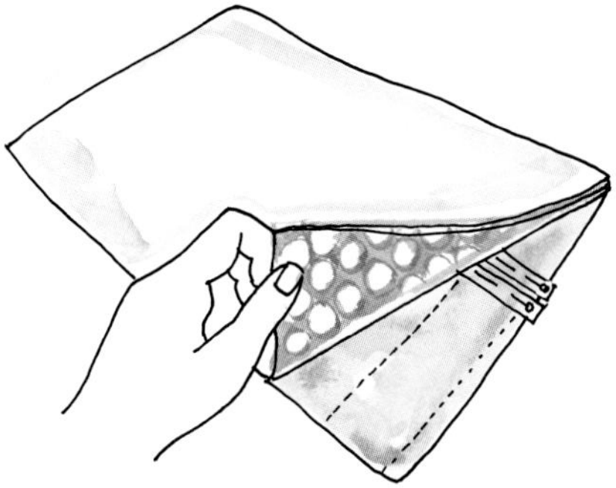

figure 1

POCKET SAVVY

When making the slots for the brush, you've got two choices:

1. Use these measurements, which will give you a variety of widths to fit your brushes: from the left side, measure 4 inches (10.2 cm), 5 inches (12.7 cm), 6 inches (15.2 cm), 7 inches (17.8 cm), 8 inches (20.3 cm), 9½ inches (24.1 cm), and 11 inches (27.9 cm).

2. Customize the slot widths to fit specific brushes. In this case, lay out your brushes, measure the widths of each one, and add ease to allow for the width of each brush.

eco chic

𝒯his little tote is the most! Not only is it made using a recycled felted sweater, but it has a double-pull drawstring mechanism using black leather lacing.

WHAT YOU NEED

Basic sewing tools

¼ yard (22.9 cm) of fabric A, cotton print for the top row of the pouch and the lining

⅛ yard (11.4 cm) of fabric B, cotton print for the middle row of the pouch

15 x 9-inch (38.1 x 22.9 cm) piece of fabric C, felted wool for the bottom row and base of the pouch

18 inches of cotton twill tape

Coordinating embroidery floss

Embroidery needle

Coordinating thread

62 inches (155 cm) of thin leather lacing

SEAM ALLOWANCE

¼ inch (6 mm) unless otherwise noted

DESIGNER

CASSI GRIFFIN

WHAT YOU DO

1 Enlarge the templates on page 304 and cut them out. Cut the fabric as described in the box below.

2 Working with purse body-1, -2, and -3 pieces, stitch fabric A to fabric B along one long edge with the right sides together. Press the seam open. With the right sides together, stitch the other long edge of fabric B to fabric C. Press the seam toward fabric B.

3 Make a tube by folding the sewn piece in half lengthwise with the right sides together, matching the seams. Pin in place and stitch. Press the seam open.

4 Turn over the top edge of the bag—fabric A—¼ inch (6 mm) and press. Turn the piece right side out.

5 Cut the twill tape into six 3-inch (7.6 cm) pieces. Fold each 3-inch (7.6 cm) piece of cotton twill tape in half to 1½ inches (3.8 cm). Pin the loops to the right side of the bag material with raw edges even, starting at the pouch seam and spacing the loops evenly.

6 Use your favorite method to assemble and attach the lining, making sure the drawstring loops are sewn between the bag fabric and the lining. Using six strands of embroidery floss and an embroidery needle, blanket stitch the felted wool base to the bottom of the pouch.

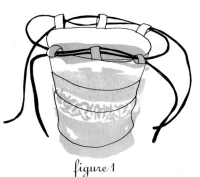

figure 1

7 Cut the lacing in half to yield two 31-inch (77.5 cm) laces. Thread the drawstring laces following the illustration (figure 1).

FIY (FELT IT YOURSELF)

Create your own felted wool for the base of this bag from an old sweater.

clutch me
tightly

DESIGNER

RENEE PARRILL

This chic clutch is full of personality—and compartments. Featuring a zippered coin purse on the inside, and two additional pockets, this clutch can help you organize your life and look good doing it.

WHAT YOU NEED

Basic sewing tools

½ yard (45.7 cm) or scrap of all-cotton quilt batting

½ yard (45.7 cm) of heavyweight interfacing

7 different fabric strips, 2 to 2½ × 20 inches (5.1 to 6.4 × 50.8 cm), cut with rotary cutter and mat

All-purpose thread

1 ¾ × 32-inch bias strip, cotton

1 yard (91.4 cm) of ⁵⁄₃₂-inch (0.4 cm) cord for piping

Cord foot or zipper foot

¾ yard (68.6 cm) of cotton ticking

9-inch (22.9 cm) zipper

Snap

Snap setter

SEAM ALLOWANCE

½ inch (1.3 cm)

WHAT YOU DO

1 Using the templates on page 306, cut out a piece of cotton batting and a piece of interfacing for both the front and back of the clutch. Place the cotton batting on top of the interfacing for both clutch pieces. Starting from the left edge of the front clutch piece, and leaving enough overhang for seam allowances on all sides, place one strip right side up. Place another strip on top of the first, right sides together, and sew about ¼ inch (0.6 cm) from the cut edge, going through all layers.

2 Repeat this process until the clutch front is pieced, and then do the same for the back piece. Trim both pieces, and make sure to leave a ½-inch (1.3 cm) seam allowance all

around. Use the pattern pieces (see the templates on pages 306 and 307) as a guide.

3 For the piping, cut a bias strip 1 ¾ × 36 inches (4.4 × 91.4 cm). Starting at the bottom center of the clutch back, wrap the bias strip around the cord and sew to the clutch with the cord foot or zipper foot. Make sure to match all cut edges, and clip the bias strip to make going around the curves easy and smooth. Join with a seam at the bottom center, cut the cord to fit, and sew the remaining piping to the clutch.

4 Cut two pieces of cotton ticking for the lining, following the clutch front and back templates on pages 306 and 307. Sew the front lining to the clutch front along the top edge, right sides together.

Open, press, and understitch to keep the lining from rolling to the outside of the clutch. Baste all raw edges together.

5 To make the zippered pocket, cut the ends off the zipper to make it 8 inches (20.3 cm) long. Make fabric stops by folding two small scraps of lining, and stitch one over each zipper end.

6 Following the pocket template on page 307, cut four pieces of the cotton ticking. Take two pieces, right sides together, and center the zipper between them at the top edge. Stitch along the zipper teeth, open, and top-stitch. Repeat on the other side of the zipper, and be sure all pieces remain lined up. Baste the raw edges together, stitching through all four layers.

A FIRM FOUNDATION

The piecing of the front and back of the clutch is an example of foundation piecing.

7 Place the zippered pocket on the lining side of the clutch front, matching the bottom edges. Baste. Place this piece on the clutch back, right sides together. Sew the pieces together, stitching inside the piping stitching as much as possible. This will hide the stitching on the right side.

8 Place the lining over the clutch so it covers the front, back, and pocket. Sew, leaving open between notches. Turn right side out, and hand stitch closed. Turn again so that the clutch is now completely right-side out. Press.

9 Add the snap at the center front of the clutch flap. Set the male part of the snap into the clutch front so it matches up with the snap on the clutch flap.

yoga*to*go

*H*ere's a way to make your fabric scraps really stretch. With straps long enough to fling over one shoulder and a zippered top to keep your mat securely snug, you'll be practicing the Downright Diva pose in no time.

DESIGNER
VALERIE SHRADER

WHAT YOU NEED

Basic sewing tools

Main fabric, ½ yard (45.7 cm)

At least 3 complementary fabrics, ¼ yard (22.9 cm) each

Matching thread

24-inch (61 cm) separating zipper in a complementary color

Zipper foot

¼-inch (0.6 cm) cord for piping, 1 yard (91.4 cm)

SEAM ALLOWANCE

Varies

7 inches (17.8 cm) square. Stack the fabrics, and cut them freehand into about four asymmetrical slices. Create a patchwork rectangle by using one strip from each section. Using a ¼-inch (0.6 cm) seam allowance, stitch the strips together, and press the seams to one side. Make at least three pieced rectangles. Trim each of the rectangles to 5 x 5 inches (12.7 x 12.7 cm). These will be placed in a staggered fashion on the carrier.

4 Cut panels in which to inset the patchwork. Each consists of three pieces, including the patchwork inset. Each finished panel should measure 5 x 16¾ inches (12.7 x 42.5 cm). Cut a strip from each of three different fabrics that is 5 x 13¾ inches (12.7 x 35 cm). Then cut each strip into two pieces with the following measurements:

- First strip: 5 x 2½ inches (12.7 x 6.4 cm) and 5 x 11¼ inches (12.7 x 28.6 cm)

- Second strip: 5 x 3½ inches (12.7 x 8.9 cm) and 5 x 10¼ inches (12.7 x 26 cm)

WHAT YOU DO

1 Cut the following: of the main fabric, two pieces each 8 x 16¾ inches (20.3 x 42.5 cm) and two circular ends 6 inches (15.2 cm) in diameter.

2 On the circular ends, mark the four spots 90° apart that are the "corners" of the circle.

3 Cut six pieces of complementary fabric (you also can include the main fabric used in this project) that are each about

- Third strip: 5 x 4½ inches (12.7 x 11.4 cm) and 5 x 9¼ inches (12.7 x 23.5 cm).

5 Sew one patchwork panel between each piece from each strip, using a ½-inch (1.3 cm) seam. Stitch the panels to one another with a ½-inch (1.3 cm) seam. For added durability, finish the seams, or use a serger to stitch them together.

6 Using the 8 x 16¾-inch (20.3 x 42.5 cm) pieces you cut in step 1, stitch them at either end of the patchwork panel, using a ½-inch (1.3 cm) seam. Trim the piece so it's 16¾ x 26 inches (42.5 x 66 cm).

7 To install the separating zipper, press under ½ inch (1.3 cm) on the long raw edges of the panel. Pin the zipper in place, and center it between the long edges. Separate the zipper, and baste each side in place by hand. Then install the zipper with the zipper foot. Note that you won't stitch a seam at either end of the zipper as with a conventional installation. Be sure to backstitch at the end of each line of stitching.

8 Make bias piping strips about 18 inches (45.7 cm) long for the ends of the carrier. (You'll discard the excess.) Baste each strip in place using a piping or zipper foot. Mark the "corners" of the carrier as you did with the ends in step 2.

9 Turn the carrier inside out, and unzip the zipper partially. With right sides together, pin the circular ends to the body of the carrier, matching the "corner" marks. Clip the carrier body as necessary. Stitch using the piping or zipper foot.

10 For the end flaps that underlie each end of the zipper, choose one of the fabrics, and cut two 2 x 6-inch (5.1 x 15.2 cm) pieces. Cut each piece in half so you have four 2 x 3-inch (5.1 x 7.6 cm) pieces. With right sides together, sew the sets of two pieces to one another, and leave one end free. Turn and press.

11 With the carrier inside out, place a flap at each end of the zipper and center it, with the raw edges even with the raw edges of the carrier. The finished end of the flap faces the opposite end of the zipper. Stitch in place on the existing ½-inch (1.3 cm) seam line.

12 To make the straps, create two patchwork strips, each 3 x 30 inches (7.6 x 76.2 cm). Fold each strip in half lengthwise with right sides facing. Stitch in a ½-inch (1.3 cm) seam, and leave one end free. Turn and trim away the seam on the short end so you can press the strap flat, and place the seam in the middle of the strap. Press under the short raw ends ¼ inch (0.6 cm), and topstitch along both sides.

13 With the carrier right side out, unzip the zipper completely. Pin one strap to the front of the carrier, and place the ends 1½ inches (3.8 cm) below the zipper and directly beside the patchwork inset. Stitch in place, and reinforce with a second line of stitching. Repeat to sew the remaining strip to the front; then stitch both straps in place at a corresponding spot at the back of the carrier.

zippin' along

$\mathscr{Y}$ou're smack dab in the middle of crafting inspiration when it hits: Where are my scissors? Instead of accusing everyone in the household, simply zip it.

DESIGNER

JOAN K. MORRIS

WHAT YOU NEED

Basic sewing tools

¼ yard (22.9 cm) of thick woven fabric

9 zippers, assorted colors, any lengths

18 inches (45.7 cm) of cording

SEAM ALLOWANCE

¼ inch (6 mm) unless otherwise noted

WHAT YOU DO

1 Enlarge the template on page 304. Check the size against your scissors and make any necessary adjustments, remembering to include the seam allowance. Cut two pieces from the woven fabric.

2 On each of the zippers, zigzag the top closed above the zipper head. To avoid breaking your needle, don't use the foot pedal. Instead, "walk" the needle across the zippers by rolling the hand wheel on the right of the machine. Lay the zippers across one of the fabric pieces as shown in figure 1, alternating the heads of the zippers. Place each zipper head with the top 3/4 inches (1.9 cm) from one edge of the fabric and mark a line on the zipper just beyond where it overlaps the opposite edge. The bottom zipper has no head, and can be cut from the other zipper ends.

figure 1

3 Starting with the top two zippers, line up the marks you made and use a tight zigzag stitch to join them with the edges butted together. Your sewing foot should fit between the zipper heads, but if it doesn't, just unzip them and move the heads. Repeat with each zipper to the bottom.

4 Place the joined zippers on top of a woven fabric piece and stitch them together very close to the edge down both sides. Cut away the unnecessary zipper ends. With a tight zigzag, stitch the edges of the top and bottom zippers to the fabric.

5 With right sides together, pin the two fabric pieces and stitch 1/4 inch (6 mm) from the side edges, down one side, around the bottom point, and up the other side. Finish the side seams by running a zigzag stitch down the length of the seam allowance on the sides and trimming any excess fabric, especially at the narrow end of the cozy.

6 Turn the piece right side out, and push out the narrow end. Leave the bottom zipper inside—this adds protection to the bottom where the scissor point goes in. Hand sew the bottom shut along the edge of the bottom outside zipper. Zigzag the top back edge of the cozy to match the zigzag edge on the front.

7 Fold the cording in half and stitch the ends to the inside top of the copy, using a zigzag stitch.

button clutchin'

Break out the buttons! This darling clutch snazzes up a simple print fabric with some serious button attitude. Cotton twill gives structure to the bag, and a decorative pleated pocket is the perfect spot for a compact or tickets for the show.

DESIGNER

REBEKA LAMBERT

WHAT YOU NEED

Basic sewing tools

½ yard (45.7 cm) of twill

¼ yard (22.9 cm) of floral fabric

¼ yard (22.9 cm) of heavyweight interfacing

1 yard (91.4 cm) of ½-inch (1.3 cm) bias tape

1 small piece of hook-and-loop tape

12 buttons

SEAM ALLOWANCE

½ inch (1.3 cm)

WHAT YOU DO

1 Enlarge the templates on page 308 and cut them out. Cut the fabric as described in the box below.

What You Cut

Twill
- 2 purse body pieces
- 2 purse lining pieces
- 1 pocket lining
- 1 flap

Floral fabric
- 1 pleated pocket
- 1 flap

Interfacing
- 2 purse body pieces

2 Transfer the pleat marks from the template to the pleated pocket fabric using straight pins. Working from the outside to the center, bring the outermost marks to the inner marks. Point the pleats toward the center of the clutch. Pin the pleats in place.

3 Place the pleated pocket with the pocket lining, wrong sides together. Adjust the pleats if necessary to match the lining dimensions.

4 Join the pocket to the lining by encasing the top edge in bias tape, as if binding a seam. Fold the bias tape over the seam allowance and hand sew the binding to the lining. Repeat with the pocket flap and flap lining, sewing along the sides and curved bottom of the flap.

5 Layer the purse pieces in the following order, from the bottom up: interfacing; purse front, right side up; pleated pocket, right side up; purse back, wrong side up; and interfacing. Line up the bottom and side edges and pin in place. Sew along the sides and bottom. Clip the corners.

6 Mark the center of the purse at the top edge of the purse back. Mark the center of the flap at the top edge. Match the purse flap to the back center with the floral side of the flap facing the right side of the purse. Pin in place along the top raw edge.

7 Use the remaining two purse body pieces and add the lining, making sure to topstitch ¼ inch (6 mm) from the top edge all around the purse.

8 Attach two small pieces of hook-and-loop tape to the pocket front and the underside of the flap. Sew buttons to the centers of the flowers.

FORMAL OR FUNKY

Embellished with identical understated buttons, this clutch has an elegant appearance, but you could make yours look more unconventional by using wild, mismatched buttons.

*you*rang?

DESIGNER

BARBARA SHEPPARD

$\mathcal{C}$ell-ebrate good times with a sassy carrier that keeps your phone at your fingertips. Made from vintage ties, it stitches up quick so you don't have to worry about going over your minutes!

WHAT YOU NEED

Basic sewing tools

Two 4-inch (10.2 cm) wide vintage neckties

10 x 14-inch (25.4 x 35.6 cm) piece of medium-weight fusible interfacing

Bias strip maker (optional)

Fabric glue

1 vintage-style button

SEAM ALLOWANCE

3/8 inch (9.5 mm) unless otherwise noted

WHAT YOU DO

1 Remove all stitching, interfacing, and lining from both neckties. Press. Decide which will be the outer fabric and which will be the lining.

2 Enlarge the templates on page 308. Cut both templates from the right side of the outer fabric and again from the wrong side of the lining fabric (figure 1). (The templates are cut this way so the strap pieces will match up correctly when placed wrong sides together.) Mark the location of the buttonhole.

figure 1

3 Cut interfacing for the outer fabric only, making sure that the fusible side matches the wrong side of each piece. Follow the manufacturer's instructions for fusing.

4 Cut a 1 1/4 x 40-inch (3.2 x 101.6 cm) bias strip from the top part of the lining tie. (Since neckties are cut on the bias, it isn't necessary to cut strips on the diagonal.) Use a bias strip maker to make a 3/8-inch (1 cm) binding. If you don't own this handy gadget, press both raw edges to the center down the length of the bias strip, fold the strip in half lengthwise, and press again.

5 Stitch the front and back outer pieces together, ending the stitch line 1/4 inch (6 mm) from the raw edge on the side with the strap, as shown (figure 2). Make a small clip through the seam allowance to this stitching on the strap piece.

Trim the seams, press them open, and turn right side out. Do the same for the lining pieces, but don't turn them right side out.

figure 2

6 Place the lining inside the case with wrong sides together. Pin and baste around the raw edges. Make a buttonhole in the strap where marked.

7 Attach the binding to the raw edge with fabric glue. Plan for the raw ends of the binding to meet at the side seam without the strap, and turn them under. You'll need to stretch the binding a bit around the curved edge of the strap to keep it from puckering. (It's helpful to use clips to hold the binding until the glue dries.) Sew the button to the front of the case.

tokyo rose

Don't you love Tokyo Rose? With a heart as big as hers, she's simply irresistible, and she'll hold all your sweet little nothings. Slip a compact, a lipstick, or some peppermints inside, and take this little flirt out on the town.

DESIGNER

NADJA GIROD

WHAT YOU NEED

Basic sewing tools

8 x 11¾-inch (20 x 30 cm) piece of heart print fabric

4 x 4-inch (10 x10 cm) piece of red felt

3¼ x 3¼-inch (8 x 8 cm) piece of white felt

4 x 4-inch (10 x10 cm) piece of black felt

5½ inch (14 cm) red zipper

15¾ inches (40 cm) of black cotton binding

Red, white, and black yarn

SEAM ALLOWANCE

½ inch (1.3 cm)

WHAT YOU DO

1 Enlarge and cut out the templates on page 309. Cut out the heart, face, hair, hands, and feet from appropriate felt colors. Embroider the eyes and mouth on the face.

2 Using the body template, cut out the purse front and back from the heart print fabric. Place the felt heart and face pieces on the front, and topstitch very close to the edges of each piece.

3 With the right sides together, attach the hands on both sides of the heart and the feet below the heart (figure 1). Pin the felt hair in place and attach with an appliqué stitch.

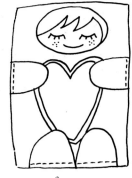

figure 1

4 Install the zipper as shown in figure 2, with the zipper wrong-side up. Repeat on the back. Finish the raw edges with binding, mitering the corners. Stitch the front to the back right sides facing.

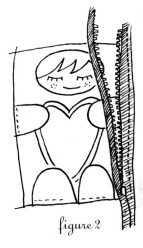

figure 2

NO RAVEL WORRIES

Felt is a great material for appliqué. You don't have to worry about binding raw edges because felt is nonwoven and doesn't ravel.

happy village

DESIGNER

AIMEE RAY

They say it takes a village, but you can create this whimsical little bag all by yourself. Be careful, though—the more you embroider, the more addicted you'll surely become!

WHAT YOU NEED

Basic sewing tools

Transfer paper

2 circles of cotton fabric, each 14 inches (35.6 cm) in diameter

Embroidery floss in 13 shades

Embroidery needle and hoop

40 inches of satin ribbon

SEAM ALLOWANCE

½ inch (1.3 cm) unless otherwise noted

WHAT YOU DO

1 Transfer the village circle embroidery pattern from page 309 to the middle of one piece of the fabric and embroider the design.

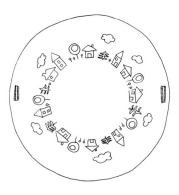

figure 1

2 Sew two buttonholes by hand with the buttonhole stitch or by machine. Place them 1½ (3.8 cm) inches from the edge of the fabric on facing sides of the embroidered circle (figure 1).

3 Line up both circles with the right sides together and stitch around the edge, leaving a small gap for turning.

4 Turn the pouch right side out and press the seams flat. Fold the raw edges in at the gap, and topstitch around the circle, close to the edge. Sew another circle 1 inch (2.5 cm) in from the edge to make a drawstring casing, making sure to sew below the buttonholes.

figure 2

5 Thread the ribbons as drawstrings through the casing (figure 2). Sew the ends of each ribbon together and slide the ribbon around in the casing so the sewn ends are hidden inside. Pull the ribbon on both sides to close the bag.

TRACE ELEMENTS

Use transfer paper to trace embroidery designs onto the fabric.

diapersnug

DESIGNER

SARAH LALONE

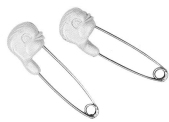

*T*aking Baby places this afternoon? Those humble diapers deserve more than a ho-hum case. Packed in this tote, they'll never get stuffed at the bottom of your wee one's travel bag.

WHAT YOU NEED

Basic sewing tools

½ yard (45.7 cm) of quilting-weight cotton (interior)

½ yard (45.7 cm) of complementary quilting-weight cotton (exterior)

½ yard (45.7 cm) of lightweight fusible interfacing

One ¾-inch (1.9 cm) button

WHAT YOU DO

1 Cut two 8 x 18-inch (20.3 x 45.7 cm) rectangles from both fabrics and the fusible interfacing. From the exterior fabric, also cut one 3 x 10-inch (7.6 x 25.4 cm) strip for the strap. From the interior fabric, cut one 1¼ x 3-inch (3.2 x 7.6 cm) strip for the button loop.

2 To make the strap, press the fabric strip in half lengthwise to make a crease. Press under each long side into the center crease and press. Refold the center crease, press, and topstitch. Fold the strap in half, press, and set aside (figure 1).

figure 1

3 Make the button loop in the same way as the strap in step 2. Fold into a loop as shown (figure 2), press, and set aside.

figure 2

4 Following the manufacturer's instructions, fuse the interfacing to the wrong side of each exterior piece of fabric. With right sides facing, pin the exterior pieces together on two long sides and one short side—the unpinned side will become the top. Measure 9 inches (22.9 cm) from the top to find the halfway point on one long side of the bag. At that spot, slip the folded strap between the two pieces and pin the raw ends in line with the edge of the bag. Stitch the three pinned sides and through the strap. Press the seams open and set aside.

5 To make the lining: With right sides facing, pin the interior rectangles together on three sides, again leaving one short side open. Stitch and press the seams open.

257

6 With both the exterior and the lining wrong side out, make boxed corners as follows:

- Cut a 1-inch (2.5 cm) square out of the bottom corners (figure 3).

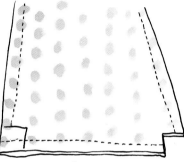

figure 3

- Refold the corners to bring the cut edges together, aligning the side and bottom seams in the middle. Pin and stitch (figure 4). Trim the seam allowance to ¼ inch (6 mm).

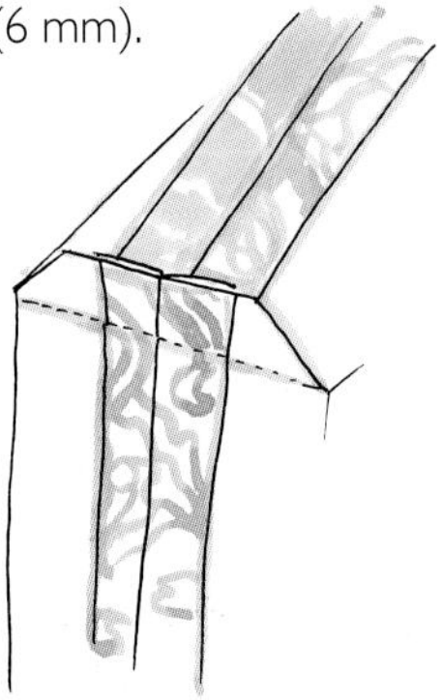

figure 4

7 For both the exterior and lining, press under the top edge 1 inch (2.5 cm). Turn the exterior right side out, and with the lining wrong side out, slip the lining into the exterior. Pin the top edges together.

8 Position the pouch with the wrist strap to the right, and locate the center of the back top edge. Tuck the raw ends of the loop between the exterior and the lining, with the loop extending outward. Edgestitch all the way around the top and through the loop.

9 Fold over the top 6 inches (15.2 cm) of the bag and press a crease for closing the pouch. On the front of the bag below the fold, mark the middle of the loop for the button placement, and hand sew the button in place.

beach baby

Life's a beach when you tote this bag. Not only is it spacious enough for a towel and tanning lotion, but it's also reversible so you can hit the boardwalk in style.

DESIGNER

NATHALIE MORNU

WHAT YOU NEED

Basic sewing tools

½ yard (45.7 cm) of fabric A, a cotton print for the bag

½ yard (45.7 cm) of fabric B, a complementary cotton print for the lining

¼ yard (22.9 cm) of fabric C, a complementary cotton stripe for the pockets

¼ yard (22.9 cm) of fabric D, a solid cotton for the bias tape and straps

SEAM ALLOWANCE

½ inch (1.3 cm) unless otherwise noted

WHAT YOU DO

1 Enlarge the templates on page 310 and cut them out.

2 Make a ¼-inch (6 mm) hem along the top of each pocket. Press the lower edge of each pocket under ½ inch (1.3 cm), clipping the curves carefully.

3 Pin a pocket, right side out, to the right side of one of the bag pieces cut from fabric A. Pin the other pocket, right side out, to the right side of one of the bag pieces cut out of fabric B. Topstitch along the sides and bottom edge of each pocket to attach it to the bag, leaving the top open. Topstitch down the center of the pocket to create two compartments.

BRAID IS AN AID

If you don't feel like making bias tape, you can use purchased fold-over braid, sold in the trimmings department of fabric stores, to bind the bag and make the straps.

4 Pin together both bag pieces cut from fabric A, with the right sides facing and matching all edges. Stitch along the curved bottom edge. Press the seam open. Repeat with fabric B to make the lining.

5 Add the lining using your favorite technique.

6 Using fabric D, make a strip of double-fold bias tape 3 inches (7.6 cm) wide and 60 inches (150 cm) long. This will be binding and straps.

7 On each side of the bag, bind the edge of the central arc—the one directly above the pocket—with a piece of bias tape. Trim off any excess tape.

8 The straps are both made from a single piece of bias tape which also encases the entire edge of the bag, and both the straps and the encasing are stitched in the same pass. Proceed as follows: Begin pinning the bias tape at one side seam, turning under the end so that when you stitch it down later, you'll get a clean seam. Work your way around the bag, pinning the tape until you reach one of the arcs where tape was applied in step 6. Leave 20 inches (50.8 cm) of bias tape loose to use as a strap. Resume binding on the other side of the arc, and continue pinning the bias tape around the edge of the bag until you reach the other arc. Again leave 20 inches (50.8 cm) of loose tape for the other strap, and resume binding on the other side

of the arc.

Continue pinning the bias tape around the edge until you reach the starting point. Cut off any excess tape and stitch the entire piece of tape. This not only attaches it to the bag, but also closes the bias tape that makes up the straps.

yo, chica

Spice up some basic corduroy with bright yo-yos and you'll be ready to strut your stuff. A magnetic closure keeps everything secure, and there's even a special little pocket inside to hold your phone.

WHAT YOU NEED

Basic sewing tools

⅓ yard (30.5 cm) of corduroy

Scrap of fabric for the phone pocket

⅓ yard (30.5 cm) of cotton print fabric for the lining and the yo-yos

Magnetic clasp

Plastic canvas, ¾ x 9 inches (9.5 x 22.9 cm)

SEAM ALLOWANCE

¼ inch (6 mm) unless otherwise noted

DESIGNER

WENDI GRATZ

What You Cut

Scrap fabric
- 2 rectangles for the pocket, each 4¼ x 3¼ inches (10.8 x 8.3 cm)

Cotton print
- 2 rectangles for the lining, each 14 x 10½ inches (35.6 x 26.7 cm)
- 1 circle 3 inches (7.6 cm) in diameter
- 1 circle 3½ inches (8.9 cm) in diameter
- 1 circle 5¼ inches (13.3 cm) in diameter

Corduroy
- 2 rectangles for the body of the purse, each 14 x 10½ inches (35.6 x 26.7 cm)
- 2 rectangles for the purse handles, each 4½ x 15 inches (11.4 x 38.1 cm)

WHAT YOU DO

1 Cut the fabric as described in the box at left. Pin the two corduroy rectangles with the right sides together and stitch around the sides and bottom. Box the bottom of the purse by flattening one bottom corner into a point, lining up the side and bottom seams. Stitch 2 inches (5.1 cm) from the point, perpendicular to the seam (figure 1). Repeat with the second corner.

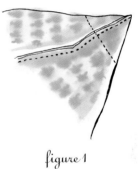

figure 1

2 Fold the edges of each handle to the center, then fold again. Topstitch. Mark the center of the purse front. Pin one end of a strap so that the inner edge is 2¼ inches (5.7 cm) from the center marking. Repeat with the other end. Pin the other strap on the purse back in the same fashion. Baste.

3 Make the cell phone pocket for the lining using your favorite method. Sew the pocket in place on one of the lining panels.

4 Make the lining as the purse, boxing the bottom as described in step 1 (page 263). Before attaching the lining to the purse, attach the magnetic clasp to the lining, following the manufacturer's instructions. Then, attach the lining with your favorite method and topstitch around the opening ¼ inch (6 mm) from the edge.

5 Make the yo-yos from the three circles of print fabric. Position the yo-yos on the bag as you wish and stitch them down by hand.

6 Place the plastic canvas in the bottom of the bag. Sew it down by hand, or leave the plastic loose if you want to be able to remove it for washing the bag.

DON'T BUDGE

Use plenty of pins when positioning corduroy for sewing— this fabric shifts a lot.

rapper wrapper

Doesn't matter whether you like hip-hop, metal, or jazz. Slip your media player inside this embroidered felt case and listen to your tunes in style.

DESIGNER

TAYLOR ANDERSON

WHAT YOU NEED

Basic sewing tools

9 x 12-inch (22.9 x 30.5 cm) piece of felt (main color)

9 x 12-inch (22.9 x 30.5 cm) piece of felt (second color)

Felt scraps in a variety of colors

2 yards (182.9 m) of embroidery floss (main color)

1 yard (91.4 m) each of embroidery floss (other colors)

2 small $3/8$-inch (9.5 mm) buttons

1 pearl-front snap

Snap applicator and hammer

WHAT YOU DO

1 Cut rectangles measuring 3 x 4 inches (7.6 x 10.2 cm) and 3 x 6 inches (7.6 x 15.2 cm) from both large felt pieces. Pin the two larger pieces together and set them aside. Cut two $1 1/4$-inch (3.2 cm) circles and three 1-inch (2.5 cm) circles from the felt scraps.

2 Plan the embellishment by laying out the felt circles on the 3 x 4-inch (7.6 x 10.2 cm) main color rectangle. The circles should be at least $1/4$ inch (6 mm) away from the edges and low enough to allow for a $1 1/2$-inch (3.8 cm) flap at the top. Use a running stitch to attach the large circles to the felt. Sew the smaller circles on top, and sew the buttons on last. If you like, use embroidery floss to backstitch a wavy, loopy line from the top left corner to the bottom right corner.

3 Pin the second 3 x 4-inch (7.6 x 10.2 cm) rectangle to the back of the embellished piece. Machine stitch the top only, as close to the edge as possible.

4 Attach the back of the snap to the center of the joined pieces, $1/4$ inch (6 mm) away from the top stitched edge. Sew the remaining 1-inch (2.5 cm) felt circle to the back, behind the back of the snap (to prevent scratches).

5 To identify what will be the flap, measure 1 1/2 inches (3.8 cm) from one end of the larger pinned rectangles. Within that space, on the color you want to be showing in front, backstitch another wavy, loopy line. Attach the front of the snap to that same side, 1/4 inch (6 mm) away from edge.

6 With wrong sides together, pin the front of the cozy to the back, with the flap of the larger piece extending past the top of the smaller piece. Stitch the sides and bottom as close to the edge as possible and trim any uneven areas.

7 Round off the corners of the flap; then blanket stitch around the edges of the flap. Insert your player and hit the road.

FREEWHEELING

If you want to access your media player while it's in the cozy, measure the size and position of the player's click wheel and screen. Cut corresponding holes through both layers of the paired rectangles. Reinforce the edges of these holes with a blanket stitch.

snap attack

This little purse proves that two snaps are better than one, and that two pockets are where it's at. The designer used Japanese silk from an old kimono, showing that your next burst of inspiration might be as close as your closet.

DESIGNER

MICHA MAE MELANCON

WHAT YOU NEED

Basic sewing tools

⅓ yard (30.5 cm) of fabric A, a Japanese silk

12 x 12-inch (30.5 x 30.5 cm) scrap of fabric B, a narrow-wale corduroy

⅓ yard (30.5 cm) of fabric C, a print cotton for lining

½ yard (45.7 cm) of lightweight fusible interfacing

⅓ yard (30.5 cm) of light- or medium-weight, non-fusible interfacing

20 inches (50.8 cm) of ½-inch (1.3 cm), double-fold bias tape

2 mother-of-pearl snaps

Snap application tools

SEAM ALLOWANCE

¼ inch (6 mm) unless otherwise noted

WHAT YOU DO

PIECING

1 Enlarge the template on page 310 and make three copies. Cut two out as they are, but turn one over so one template has a left flap and one has a right flap. For the third template, cut off the flap—this is the purse front.

2 Cut fabric A into three pieces at least 1 inch (2.5 cm) larger all around than the template; cut the same of fusible interfacing. Cut three identical pieces of fusible interfacing. Cut an additional piece of interfacing using the fabric B piece as a pattern. Apply the interfacing pieces to the wrong side of each fabric piece.

3 Working with a fabric A piece for the purse front, cut the piece in two at an angle. Cut a tapered strip of fabric B at least the length of the diagonal cut of silk. Cut the length against the wale so the ribbing runs horizontally across the width.

4 Position the tapered strip along one diagonal cut of fabric A with the right sides together. Stitch along the edge. On the wrong side of the fabric, press the seam allowance toward fabric A. Topstitch close to the seam on the right side of fabric A. Press again if needed. Attach the strip to the other piece of fabric A in the same way.

5 Repeat step 4 with the fabric A piece for the left flap panel and right flap panel. Make a second cut in those pieces as well, inserting a fabric B strip across the area for the flap itself.

ASSEMBLING

1 Cut one of each template (purse front, left flap panel, right flap panel) from the pieced materials. Cut one of each template from the fabric C lining, and cut one of each template from the non-fusible interfacing.

2 Place the fabric A panel right side up, position the fabric C lining wrong side up over it, and place the front panel interfacing on top of that. Sew across the top edge. Turn right side out and press the seam. Topstitch along the edge, close to the seam.

3 Repeat step 2 for the right flap panel pieces and the left flap panel pieces. Sew along the top edge, following the curve of the flap. Notch the curved edges and corners of each flap to help the seam allowances lie flat and tidy. Turn right side out and press. Topstitch along the top edge.

4 After completing all three pieces, position the left flap panel with the silk side up. Place the right flap panel on top of it with the silk side up. Place the front on top of that with the fabric C lining side up. Carefully line up all straight edges. Sew the three panels together along the unfinished edges of the bottom curve. Trim any irregular edges.

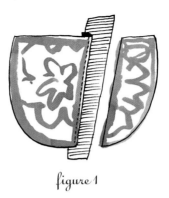

figure 1

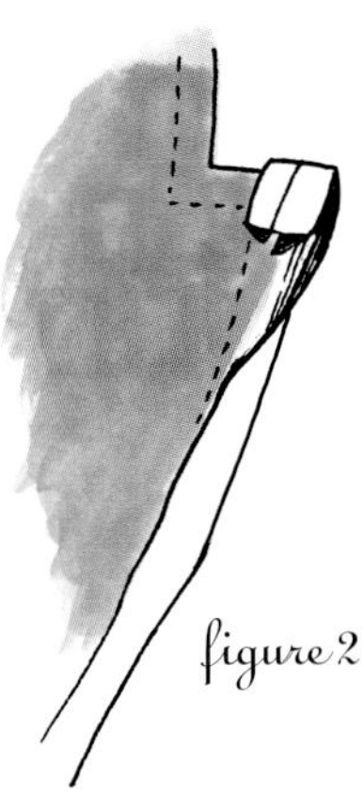

figure 2

5 Cut a 20-inch (50.8 cm) strip of ½-inch (1.3 cm) double-fold bias tape (figure 1). Bind the unfinished curved seam allowance just sewn and miter the top corners as shown above (figure 2).

6 Apply a snap to each flap following the manufacturer's instructions. Since the flaps overlap, start with the right flap, which is underneath. Apply the top snap to the flap. Fold the flap over and trace the tip of the stud with a fabric pencil. Use this mark to apply the other half of the snap. Repeat for the left flap.

TOUCHY FEELY

This purse uses silk and fine-wale corduroy for a great textural contrast. Use other fabrics if you like, but to add interest make sure they have different textures or sheen.

inthebag

$\mathcal{D}$rawn to this bag? It's no wonder. With the adjustable drawstring design, you can carry as little, or as much, as you like. A pretty ribbon cinch-pull with beads tops it off and ties it all together.

DESIGNER

REBEKA LAMBERT

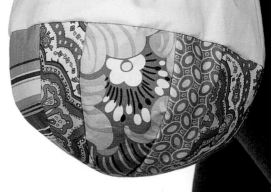

WHAT YOU NEED

Basic sewing tools

⅓ yard (30.5 cm) of muslin

½ yard (45.7 cm) fusible interfacing

½ yard (45.7 cm) floral fabric

⅛ yard (11.4 cm) each of 5 different fabrics in complementary colors

Thread

1⅔ yard (152 cm) of ⅜-inch (1 cm) ribbon

Safety pin

2 beads each of 2 different colors

SEAM ALLOWANCE

Varies

WHAT YOU DO

1 Use the rotary cutter, ruler, and cutting mat to cut two 10 x 12-inch (25.4 x 30.5 cm) rectangles from the muslin. Do the same from the interfacing. From the floral fabric, cut a 15½ x 23-inch (26 x 58.4 cm) rectangle.

2 From each of the five printed fabrics, cut out a narrow and a wide wedge piece, using the templates on page 311 as your guide, for a total of ten pieces. Then cut out five narrow wedges and five wide wedges from the interfacing. Fuse the interfacing according to the manufacturer's instructions to the back of the wedges and muslin.

3 From the five printed fabrics, cut out a total of nine 1 x 3-inch (2.5 x 7.6 cm) rectangles and eight 2½ x 3-inch (6.4 x 7.6 cm) rectangles, varying the fabrics.

4 Place two patchwork wedge pieces right sides together. Sew along one long side, using a ¼-inch (0.6 cm) seam allowance (figure 1). Open the pieces with the right sides facing up. Place another wedge face down on top of one of the sewn wedges. Line up the raw edges, and then stitch using a ¼-inch (0.6 cm) seam allowance. Repeat for all wedges until a bowl is formed.

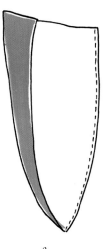

figure 1

5 Sew the fabric rectangles from step 3 together, alternating 1-inch-wide (2.5 cm) and 2½-inch-wide (6.4 cm) rectangles, with a ¼-inch (0.6 cm) seam allowance. You'll have a strip 3 inches (7.6 cm) wide and about 10½ inches (26.7 cm) long. Then cut the patchwork strip in half lengthwise to make two 10½ x 1½-inch (26.7 x 3.8 cm) strips to create a channel for the drawstring.

6 For each strip from step 5, with the wrong side facing up, fold the long sides to the center, then press. Fold each short side over ¼ inch (0.6 cm). Press. Stitch each short end. The finished patchwork channel should be ¾ x 10 inches (1.9 x 25.4 cm).

7 Pin a patchwork strip, right side up, to the right side of one of the muslin rectangles. The strip should be positioned parallel with the 12-inch (30.5 cm) side, and it should be 3½ inches (8.9 cm) from the top with 1 inch (2.5 cm) of muslin on either end. Then sew the patchwork channel to the muslin, close to the edge, along the long sides of the strip. Repeat with the other piece of muslin and patchwork strip.

8 With the right sides of the muslin together, line up the raw edges and the patchwork channels. Stitch along the sides of the muslin using a ½-inch (1.3 cm) seam allowance.

9 Place the patchwork "bowl" inside the bottom of the muslin body, right sides facing each other. Stitch all around the bowl to join the two together.

10 Make the bag's lining by folding the floral fabric (as cut in step 1) in half, right sides together, lining up the short ends of the rectangle. Stitch along the short end to form a tube. With a needle, thread, and running stitch, gather one end of the tube.

11 Turn the bag body wrong side out and the lining right side out. Place the lining inside the bag body. Sew along the top of the bag ½ inch (1.3 cm) from the edge, and leave a 5-inch (12.7 cm) section unsewn, to be used for turning.

12 Reach through the opening, and pull the lining through the hole, turning the bag right side out. Then press the raw edges of the opening ½ inch (1.3 cm) to the inside, and pin in place. Stitch along the top edge ¼ inch (0.6 cm) from the edge, and be sure to sew up the opening.

13 Cut the ribbon into two equal lengths, and fasten the safety pin onto one end. Starting on one side of the bag, thread a piece of ribbon through both patchwork channels. Repeat, starting on the opposite side of the bag with the other piece of ribbon. For each side, string beads on the ends of the ribbon, and then tie the two ends together with a knot.

273

sweetstash

For a double shot of crafty cool, make your own cup hugger with a special stash pocket for your frequent sipper card, a teabag, or sugar packets. Break time has never been so sweet!

DESIGNER

GIGI THORSEN

WHAT YOU NEED

Basic sewing tools

4¹/₂ x 12-inch (11.4 x 30.5 cm) scrap of outer fabric

4¹/₂ x 12-inch (11.4 x 30.5 cm) scrap of fleece 3-inch (7.6 cm) square of contrasting fabric for the pocket

Fabric glue (optional)

1 decorative button

SEAM ALLOWANCE

¹/₄ inch (6 mm) unless otherwise noted

WHAT YOU DO

1 Enlarge the template on page 311. Cut one piece from the outer fabric and one from the fleece.

2 With right sides together, pin the outer fabric to the fleece. Stitch the top and bottom edges. Trim the seam allowance, turn the cozy right side out, and press. Topstitch the top and bottom seams as close to the edge as possible.

3 Turn under all four sides of the pocket square ¹/₄ inch (6 mm), using a few dabs of fabric glue if desired. Trim the folded corners with scissors so the excess doesn't peek out.

4 Mark the spot for the button placement, and sew the button to the pocket. Pin the pocket in place and stitch.

5 Place the ends of the cozy together, fleece side facing out. Use fabric glue or pins to hold in place, and stitch the ends together. Trim the seam allowance and finish the raw edges with a zigzag stitch. Time for a well-deserved coffee break.

weallscream

DESIGNER

KELLEY GRACE
QUAKKELAAR

*P*eople who can't be bothered to scoop their dessert into a bowl—you know who you are, and there ain't no shame—will shout for joy. No more frozen fingertips! That problem solved, you can address more important issues: which flavor?

WHAT YOU NEED

Basic sewing tools

4 x 13½-inch (10.2 x 34.3 cm) piece of fabric

4½ x 13½-inch (11.4 x 34.3 cm) piece of fleece

SEAM ALLOWANCE

⅜ inch (9.5 mm) unless otherwise noted

WHAT YOU DO

1 With right sides together, line up the top edge of the fabric with the fleece, pin, and stitch.

2 Match up the bottom edges—the fleece will have a bump in it, since you want an edge of fleece showing along the top and bottom of the fabric when finished. Pin the pieces together so they don't shift, and stitch the bottom seam.

3 Turn the cozy right side out and press the edges lightly with an iron. Make sure you have an even border of fleece along the top and bottom of the fabric. Topstitch both edges.

4 Enlarge the template on page 311. Fold the cozy with right sides together and lay the tem-plate on top. Align the template "fold" edge with the folded cozy, and make sure the wider end matches up with the top of your fabric. Trace the pattern onto the fabric with chalk and stitch along that line. Trim the excess seam allowance, turn right side out, and head for the fridge.

handy hook holder

$\mathcal{H}$ooked on crochet? Then this little holder is just for you. Don't know how? Don't dismay—this multi-functional design is also perfect for stashing pens, drawing pencils, manicure sets, makeup brushes and more.

WHAT YOU NEED

Basic sewing tools

⅓ yard (30.5 cm) black-striped ticking

⅓ yard (30.5 cm) striped ticking in another color

Thread

2 skeins matching perle cotton or embroidery floss

Self-covering button kit

SEAM ALLOWANCE

⅜ inch (1 cm)

DESIGNER

TERRY TAYLOR

278

WHAT YOU DO

TO MAKE THE INSIDE:

1 Cut one 12¾ x 9¾-inch (32.4 x 24.7 cm) piece of fabric with the ticking stripes running horizontally.

2 Cut one 12¾ x 5¾-inch (32.4 x 14.6 cm) piece of fabric with the ticking stripes running vertically. Turn and press one long side of the fabric with a ⅜-inch (1 cm) hem.

3 Place the hemmed piece on top of the larger piece. Using the stripes as a guide, stitch along the stripes to create pockets for your hooks. Note that this project calls for seam allowances of ⅜ inch (1 cm).

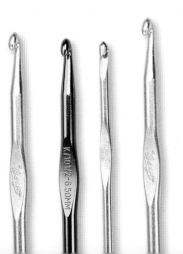

TO MAKE THE OUTSIDE:

4 Cut 12 strips of ticking measuring 2½ x 5½ inches (6.4 x 14 cm) wide. Cut some strips with horizontal stripes, some with vertical stripes.

5 Stack two strips together and stitch along one of the 2½-inch (6.4 cm) ends. Create five more long, two-piece strips in the same way.

6 Arrange the longer strips together as desired. Stitch the long sides together.

7 Embellish the strips with bold running stitches as desired.

TO MAKE THE BUTTON LOOP:

8 Cut a 1 x 4-inch (2.5 x 10.2 cm) strip of fabric. Fold and press the strip in half lengthwise. Open the strip and fold the raw edges in to the crease. Fold the two sides together and stitch the open edges together.

9 Form a U-shaped loop with the fabric. Place the loop on the lower third of the inside fabric, with the loop on top of the fabric. Adjust the size of the loop as desired, and then pin it in place. Trim the ends if needed.

10 Stitch the ends of the loop in place.

ASSEMBLY:

11 Place the inside and outside fabrics right sides together. Pin them in place.

12 To create rounded corners, mark the corners using a coin before you stitch the pieces together.

13 Stitch the two layers together, leaving an opening on the short side with the loop unstitched. You will need the opening in order to turn the assembly right side out.

14 Clip and trim the rounded corners. You may wish to trim the raw edges to reduce bulk.

15 Turn the piece right sides out. Hand stitch the opening closed.

TO MAKE THE BUTTON:

16 Cut a piece of fabric to the size needed for your button.

17 Embellish the fabric with running stitches as desired.

18 Assemble the button according to the manufac-turer's instructions.

19 Stitch the button in place about 2½ inches (6.4 cm) in on the side opposite the loop.

TO FINISH:

20 Place your hooks in the pockets, fold the fabric down from the top, fold over the sides, and slip the loop over the button.

dream on

Tired of the same old purses?
Try making one from a vintage pillowcase.
With an oversize pleated bow and a
zippered closure, this clutch is
the stuff of dreams.

DESIGNER

REBEKA LAMBERT

WHAT YOU NEED

Basic sewing tools

¼ yard (22.9 cm) heavyweight fusible interfacing

2 vintage pillowcases (or ¼ yard [22.9 m] of cotton fabric in each color)

12-inch (30.5 cm) zipper

5 inches (12.7 cm) of ribbon

SEAM ALLOWANCE

½ inch (1.3 cm) unless otherwise noted

What You Cut

One of the pillowcases (or fabric)
- *2 pieces 12 x 7 inches (30.5 x 17.8 cm)*

Other pillowcase (or fabric)
- *2 pieces 12 x 7 inches (30.5 x 17.8 cm)*
- *1 piece 14 x 12 inches (35.6 x 30.5 cm)*
- *1 piece 3½ x 4½ inches (8.9 x 11.4 cm)*

Interfacing
- *2 pieces 12 x 7 inches (30.5 x 17.8 cm)*

WHAT YOU DO

1 Cut the fabric as described in the box at bottom left. Fuse the interfacing pieces to the wrong side of the 12 x 7-inch (30.5 x 17.8 cm) pieces of fabric following the manufacturer's instructions.

2 Using the 14 x 12-inch (35.6 x 30.5 cm) rectangle, fold over 1/8 inch (3 mm) on one long edge. Fold over ⅛ inch (3 mm) again and press. Sew the narrow hem. Repeat for the other long edge.

3 Fold the 3½ x 4½-inch (8.9 x 11.4 cm) piece of fabric in half lengthwise with the right sides together. Sew the 3½-inch (8.9 cm) side together. Turn right side out and center the seam. Keeping the seam on the outside, fold the tube in half, matching the raw edges. Sew a seam along the raw edge, creating a ring. Turn the sewn ring inside out so the seam with the raw edge is on the inside of the ring.

4 Lay the large hemmed rectangle horizontally and right side up. Gather the center, accordion style, and slip the sewn ring over one end, sliding it into place in the center to create the bow for the purse front (figure 1).

5 Choose one of the rectangles as the purse front and mark its center point. Position the bow center over the center point on the purse front. Pin each corner of the bow ½ inch (1.3 cm) from the top and bottom edges of the purse front.

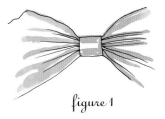

figure 1

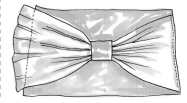

figure 2

6 Arrange the gathers of the bow along the sides of the clutch. Baste along the side edges to keep the gathers in place. Trim the excess bow fabric (figure 2).

7 Install the zipper, add the lining, and finish using your favorite method. Thread the ribbon through the zipper pull and knot it.

WHITE SALE

You can find bed linens in great retro prints for next to nothing at almost any thrift store.

undercover

$\mathcal{D}$ear Diary, I haven't written in a while, but today I made you the prettiest case. Inside, I stitched a large pocket to slide you into. Opposite that are tabs for pen-holders and more pockets for note cards. Now, I have to tell you about this hottie I just met....

DESIGNER

HELEN ANGHARAD HENLEY

WHAT YOU NEED

Basic sewing tools

¼ yard (22.9 cm) of linen

¼ yard (22.9 cm) of cotton print

¼ yard (22.9 cm) of cotton flannel or brushed cotton

½ yard (44.7 cm) of heavyweight fusible interfacing

6 inches (15.2 cm) of ¼-inch (6 mm) gingham ribbon

1 button

SEAM ALLOWANCE

¼ inch (6 mm) unless otherwise noted

WHAT YOU DO

1 Cut out the fabrics as follows.

- **From the linen**
One 8 x 12-inch (20.3 x 30.5 cm) rectangle (outside of cozy)

One 8-inch (20.3 cm) square (inside right pocket)

- **From the cotton print**
One 8 x 12-inch (20.3 x 30.5 cm) rectangle (interior of cozy)

One 8 x 11-inch (20.3 x 27.9 cm) rectangle (inside left diary flap)

One 8 x 6-inch (20.3 x 15.2 cm) rectangle (inside right pocket)

One 3½ x 5-inch (8.9 x 12.7 cm) rectangle (penholder)

One 3½ x 8-inch (8.9 x 20.3 cm) rectangle outside embellishment panel)

- **From the cotton flannel**
One 8 x 12-inch (20.3 x 30.5 cm) rectangle (padding)

- **From the interfacing**
One 8 x 11-inch (20.3 x 2.9 cm) rectangle

One 8-inch (20.3 cm) square

One 8 x 6-inch (20.3 x 15.2 cm) rectangle

One 3½ x 5-inch (8.9 x 12.7 cm) rectangle

One 3½ x 8-inch (8.9 x 20.3 cm) rectangle

2 Following the manufacturer's instructions, fuse the interfacing to the wrong side of all pieces cut from the cotton print fabric, except for the interior of the cozy. Also fuse interfacing to the wrong side of the linen inside pocket square.

3 To make the inside right pocket panel, fold the cotton piece in half lengthwise, wrong sides together, to make an 8 x 3-inch (20.3 x 7.6 cm) piece. Press and then edgestitch along the folded edge. Do the same for the linen pocket square, folding it in half and edgestitching the fold. With both sides facing up, pin the cotton piece on top of the linen, aligning them on the right. Measure to find the midway point and stitch across the cotton fabric. Set aside.

4 To make the inside left diary flap, fold the piece in half as in step 3, making an 8 x 5½-inch (20.3 x 14 cm) folded piece. Press and stitch the folded edge as before. Set aside.

5 To make the penholder, press under the edges of the fabric ¼ inch (6 mm) on all sides. Fold it in half lengthwise, wrong sides together, and edgestitch on all four sides. Set aside.

6 To embellish the cozy exterior: with both sides facing up, lay the cotton flannel piece lengthwise left to right, and pin the linen rectangle on top. Press under ¼ inch (6 mm) on the two long sides of the embellishment panel. Measure 2 inches (5.1 cm) from the right edge of the linen rectangle and position the edge of the panel there, aligning the short edges with the edges of the linen. Pin in place and topstitch all four sides of the panel as close to the edge as possible, stitching through all layers. Stitch a series of parallel lines across the panel, using the edge of your presser foot as a guide.

7 Assemble the pieces by first laying out the interior cotton piece, right side up. For the penholder placement, mark with a pin or chalk where the cozy will fold in the middle. The left edge of the penholder will be positioned at the fold about 2 inches (5.1 cm) from the top edge of the cozy. Mark this spot.

Press under both short ends of the penholder ½ inch (1.3 cm). Pin one end at the fold where marked, and pin the other end 2¾ inches (7 cm) to the right, which leaves some slack in between. Stitch a narrow rectangle over the folds at both ends. Place two pens under the loop of fabric to mark where you need to stitch the slots. Stitch a small rectangle through all the layers at this central point (figure 1).

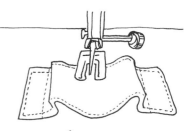

figure 1

8 Pin the left flap and the right pocket panel to the right side of the interior, aligning the outer raw edges. (The left edge of the pocket panel will slightly overlap the penholder strip.) Baste the pocket pieces in place.

9 Fold the gingham ribbon in half to form a loop. Pin the ends at the halfway point on the right-hand side pocket and baste in place. Pin down the folded end to keep it out of the way.

10 Lay the exterior cozy piece on top of the interior and pocket pieces with the right sides facing. Position the side with the embellishment to the left (figure 2).

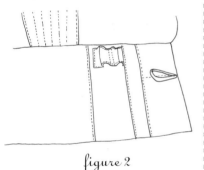

figure 2

Pin the layers together and start stitching on the left-hand side about 2 inches (5.1 cm) from the top edge of the fabric. Stitch through all layers all the way around the cozy, leaving a 3-inch (7.6 cm) opening for turning.

11 Clip the corners, trim the seam allowance, and turn the cozy right side out through the opening. Push out the corners and press the cozy inside and out, turning in the seam allowance at the opening. Edgestitch all the way around the cozy, closing the opening.

12 Fold the cozy closed and mark where the button needs to be aligned with the ribbon loop. Hand sew the button in place.

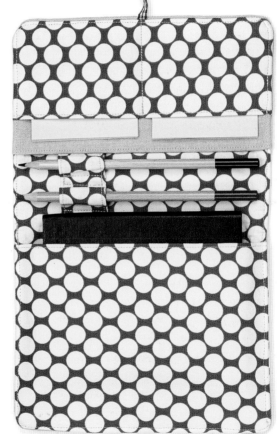

Templates

Feeling Needled, page 18

(enlarge 200% or size as desired)

Man

Woman

Square Deal, page 54

(enlarge 400%)

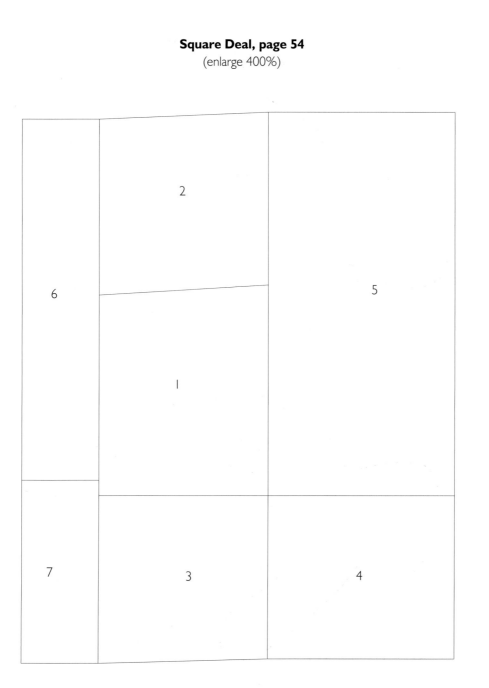

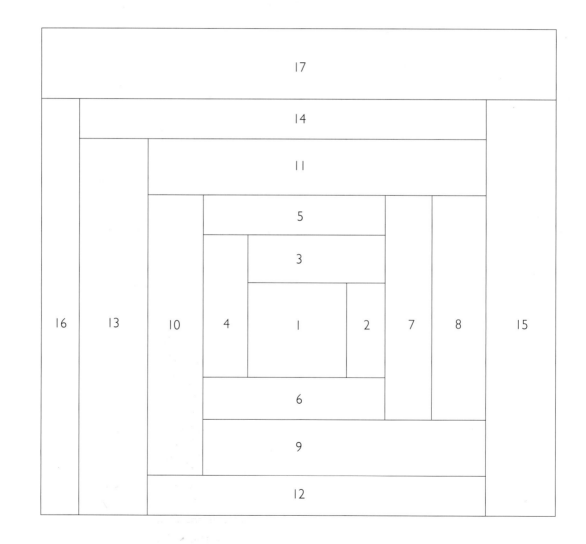

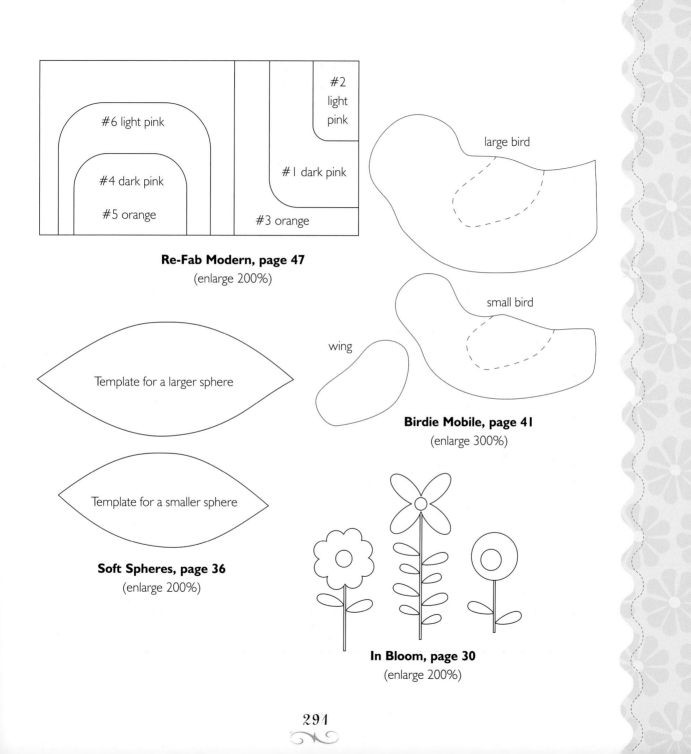

#6 light pink

#4 dark pink

#5 orange

#2 light pink

#1 dark pink

#3 orange

Re-Fab Modern, page 47
(enlarge 200%)

large bird

small bird

wing

Birdie Mobile, page 41
(enlarge 300%)

Template for a larger sphere

Template for a smaller sphere

Soft Spheres, page 36
(enlarge 200%)

In Bloom, page 30
(enlarge 200%)

Yard Tale, page 32

Vegetables, actual size

Door, actual size

Garden, enlarge 300%

Clothes, actual size

Tree, enlarge 300%

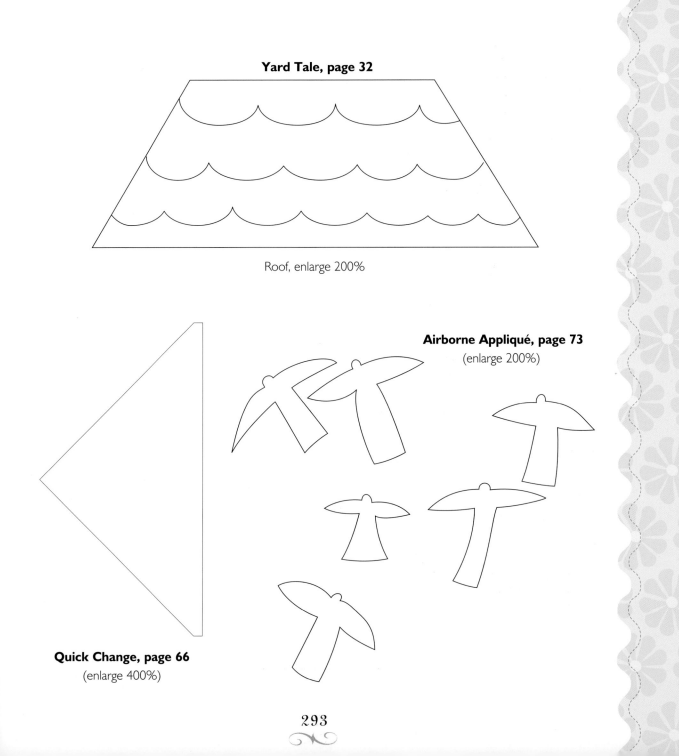

Yard Tale, page 32

Roof, enlarge 200%

Airborne Appliqué, page 73
(enlarge 200%)

Quick Change, page 66
(enlarge 400%)

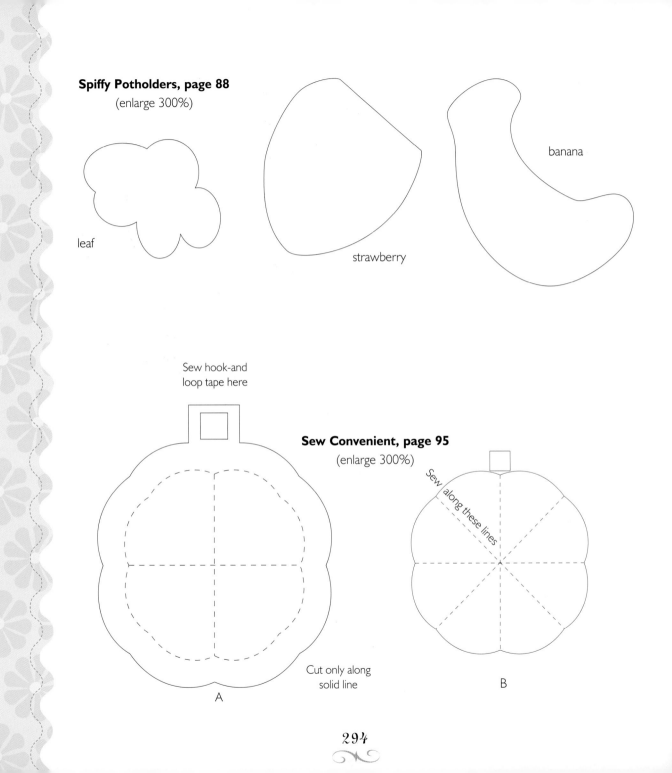

Spiffy Potholders, page 88
(enlarge 300%)

leaf

strawberry

banana

Sew hook-and
loop tape here

Sew Convenient, page 95
(enlarge 300%)

Sew along these lines

Cut only along
solid line

A

B

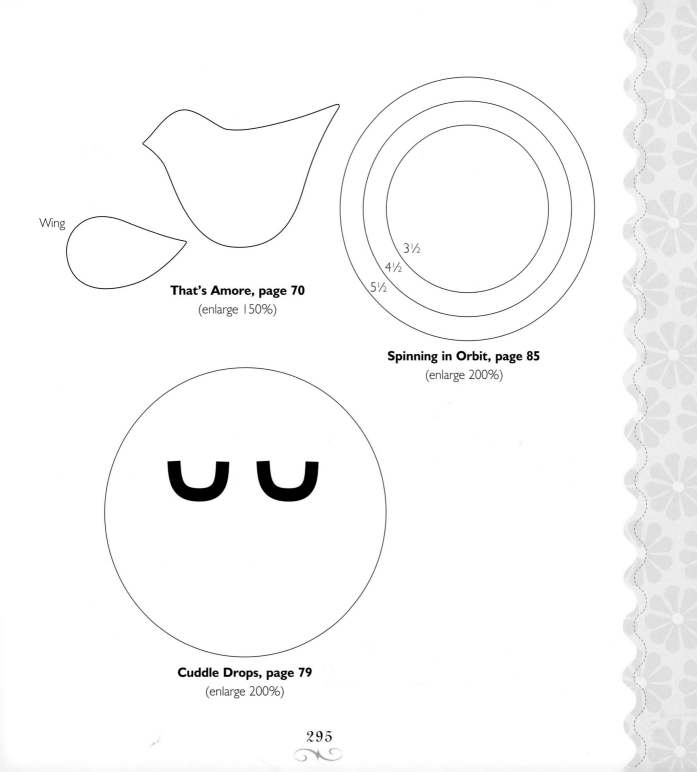

Wing

That's Amore, page 70

(enlarge 150%)

3½

4½

5½

Spinning in Orbit, page 85

(enlarge 200%)

Cuddle Drops, page 79

(enlarge 200%)

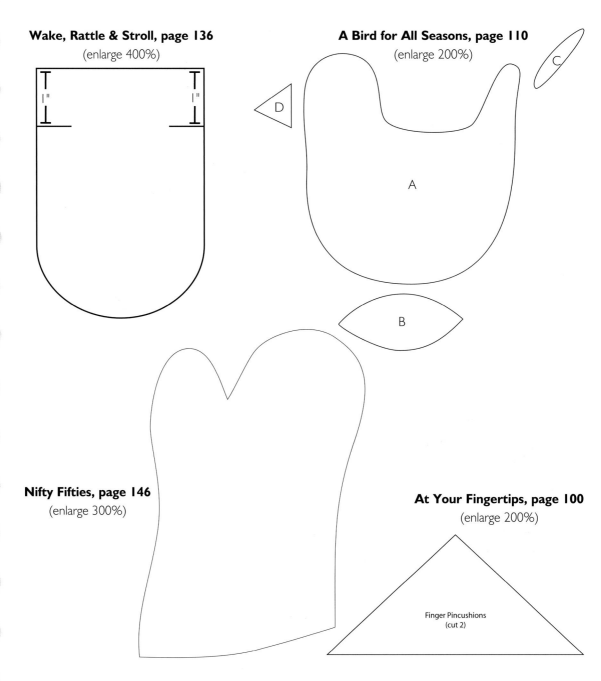

Wake, Rattle & Stroll, page 136
(enlarge 400%)

1"

1"

A Bird for All Seasons, page 110
(enlarge 200%)

C

D

A

B

Nifty Fifties, page 146
(enlarge 300%)

At Your Fingertips, page 100
(enlarge 200%)

Finger Pincushions
(cut 2)

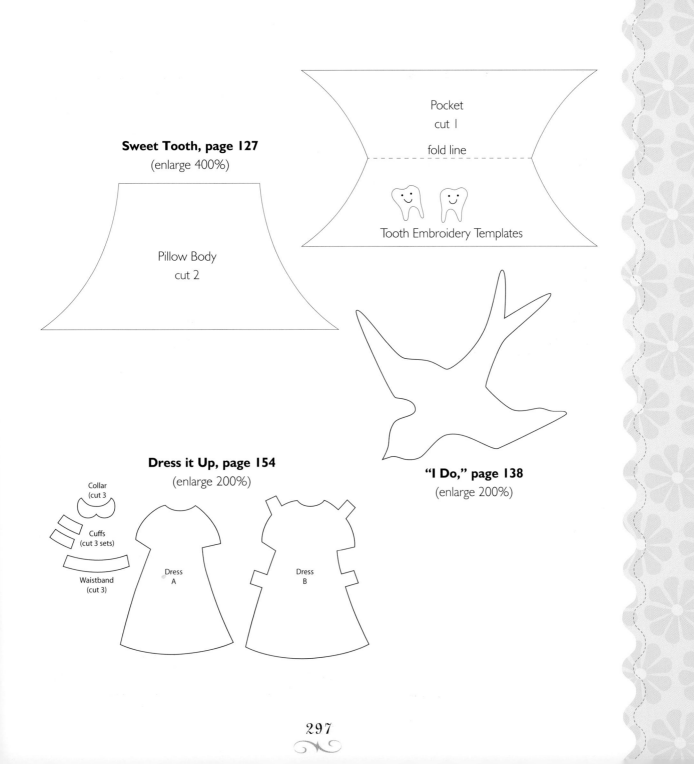

Sweet Tooth, page 127

(enlarge 400%)

Pillow Body
cut 2

Pocket
cut 1

fold line

Tooth Embroidery Templates

Dress it Up, page 154

(enlarge 200%)

Collar
(cut 3)

Cuffs
(cut 3 sets)

Waistband
(cut 3)

Dress
A

Dress
B

"I Do," page 138

(enlarge 200%)

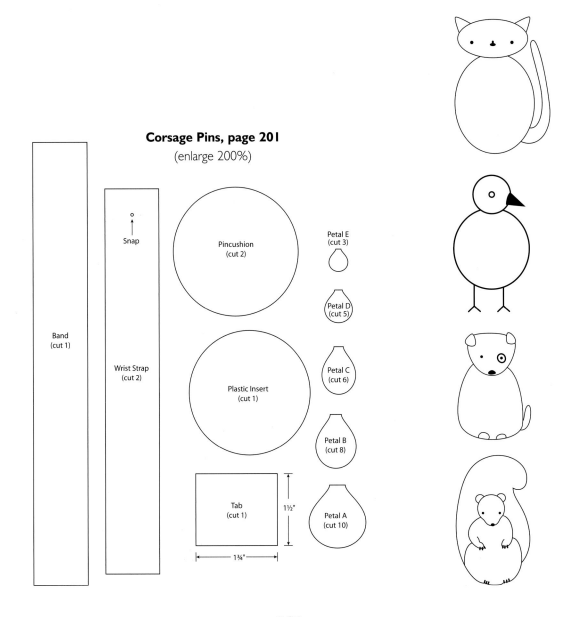

Pinning Zoo, page 176
(enlarge as desired)

Corsage Pins, page 201
(enlarge 200%)

Band
(cut 1)

Snap

Wrist Strap
(cut 2)

Pincushion
(cut 2)

Plastic Insert
(cut 1)

Tab
(cut 1)

1½"

1¾"

Petal E
(cut 3)

Petal D
(cut 5)

Petal C
(cut 6)

Petal B
(cut 8)

Petal A
(cut 10)

Nifty Fifties, page 144
(full scale)

Salsa Softies, page 180
(enlarge 400%)

Scorchin'! page 185
(enlarge 300%)

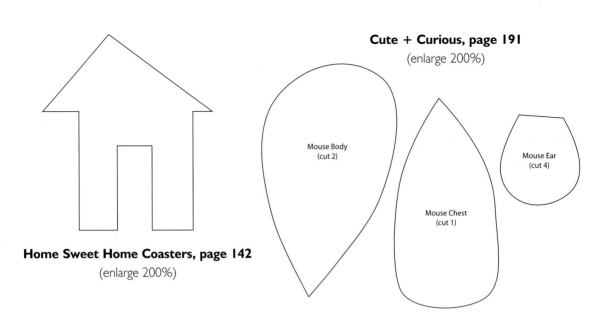

Cute + Curious, page 191
(enlarge 200%)

Mouse Body
(cut 2)

Mouse Chest
(cut 1)

Mouse Ear
(cut 4)

Home Sweet Home Coasters, page 142
(enlarge 200%)

Ribbon Rounds, page 182
(enlarge 200%)

Bee Sewing, page 162
(enlarge 200%)

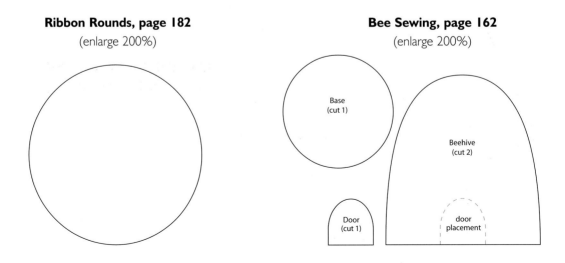

Base
(cut 1)

Beehive
(cut 2)

Door
(cut 1)

door
placement

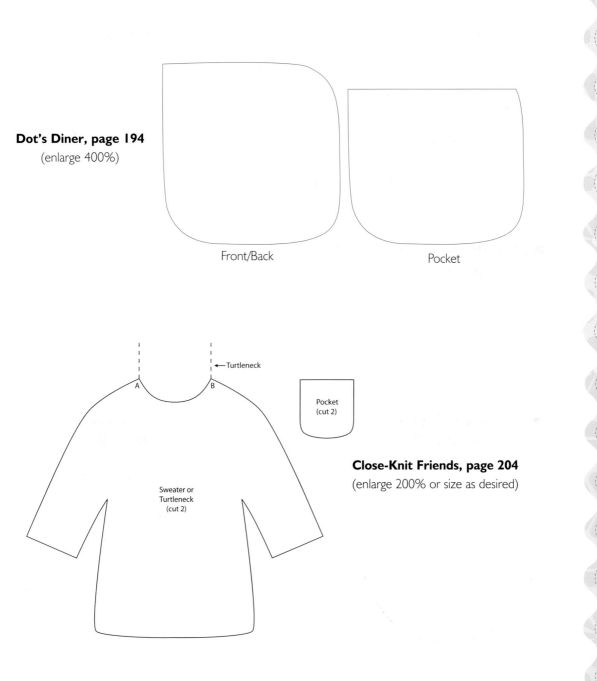

Dot's Diner, page 194

(enlarge 400%)

Front/Back

Pocket

←Turtleneck

A

B

Sweater or
Turtleneck
(cut 2)

Pocket
(cut 2)

Close-Knit Friends, page 204

(enlarge 200% or size as desired)

All Buttoned Up, page 178

(enlarge 200%)

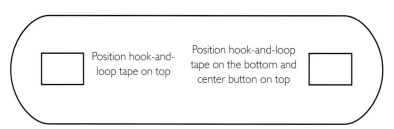

Position hook-and-loop tape on top

Position hook-and-loop tape on the bottom and center button on top

Card Cache, page 222

(enlarge 200%)

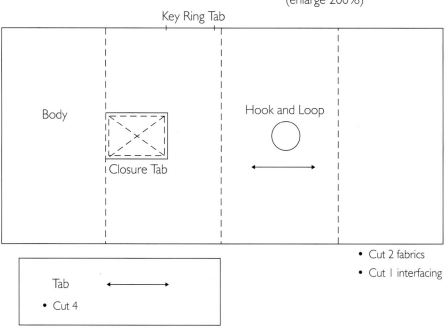

Key Ring Tab

Body

Hook and Loop

Closure Tab

- Cut 2 fabrics
- Cut 1 interfacing

Tab

- Cut 4

Spot On, page 218
(enlarge 200%)

Sweet Treat, page 206
(enlarge 200%)

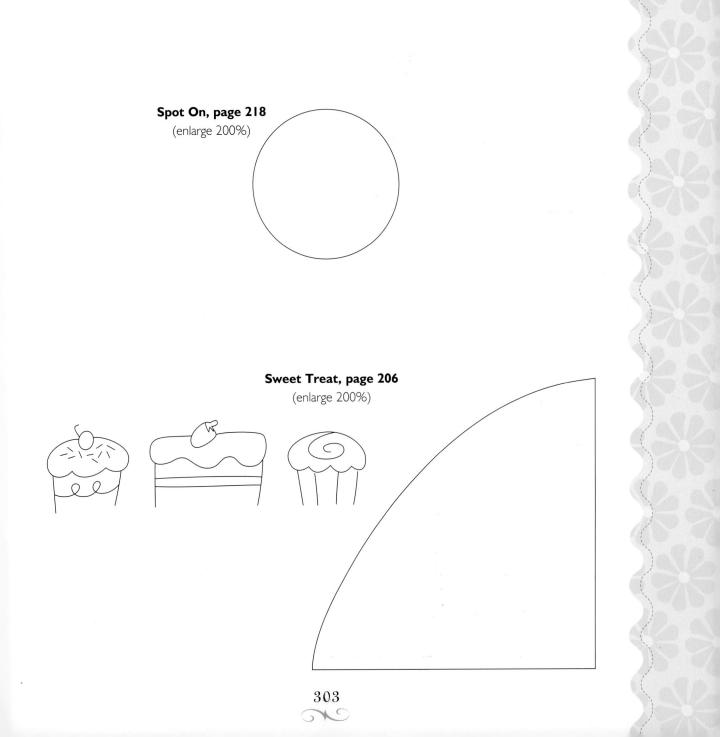

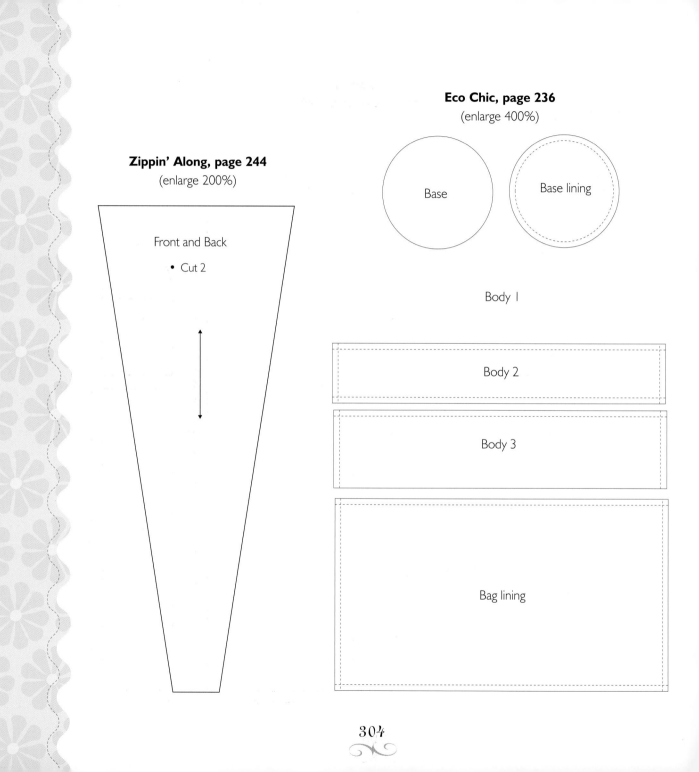

Zippin' Along, page 244

(enlarge 200%)

Front and Back

• Cut 2

Eco Chic, page 236

(enlarge 400%)

Base

Base lining

Body 1

Body 2

Body 3

Bag lining

Pin Pals, page 210

(enlarge 200% or as desired)

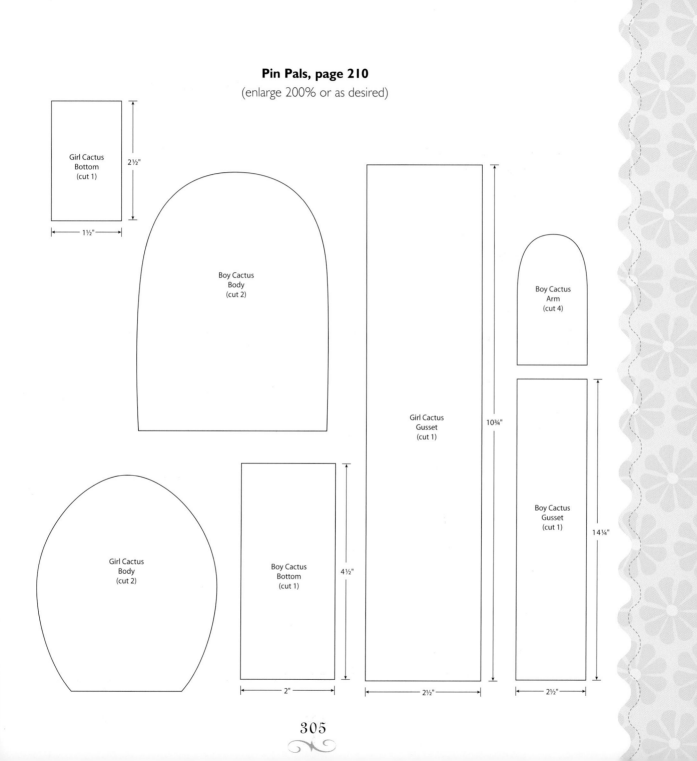

Girl Cactus
Bottom
(cut 1)

2½"

1½"

Boy Cactus
Body
(cut 2)

Boy Cactus
Arm
(cut 4)

Girl Cactus
Gusset
(cut 1)

10¾"

Boy Cactus
Gusset
(cut 1)

14¼"

Girl Cactus
Body
(cut 2)

Boy Cactus
Bottom
(cut 1)

4½"

2"

2½"

2½"

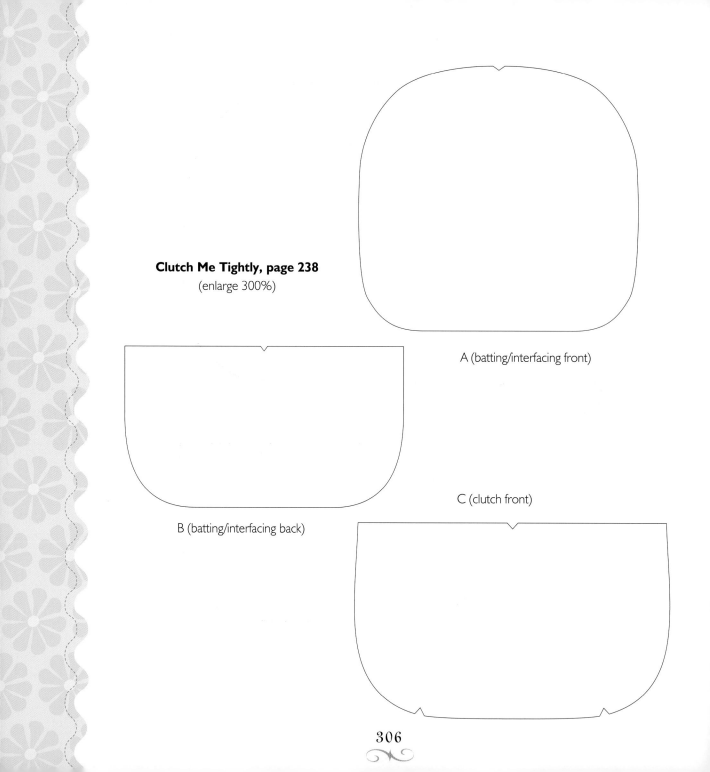

Clutch Me Tightly, page 238
(enlarge 300%)

A (batting/interfacing front)

B (batting/interfacing back)

C (clutch front)

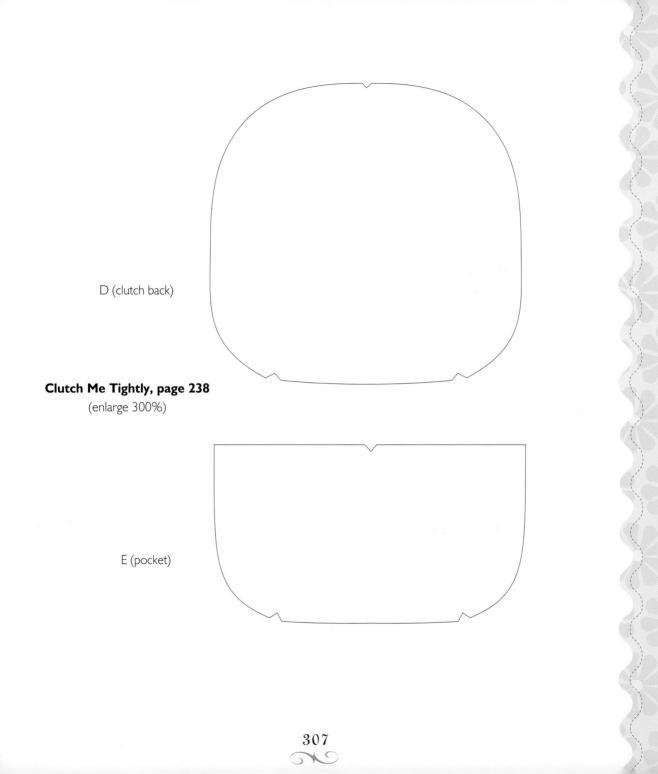

D (clutch back)

Clutch Me Tightly, page 238
(enlarge 300%)

E (pocket)

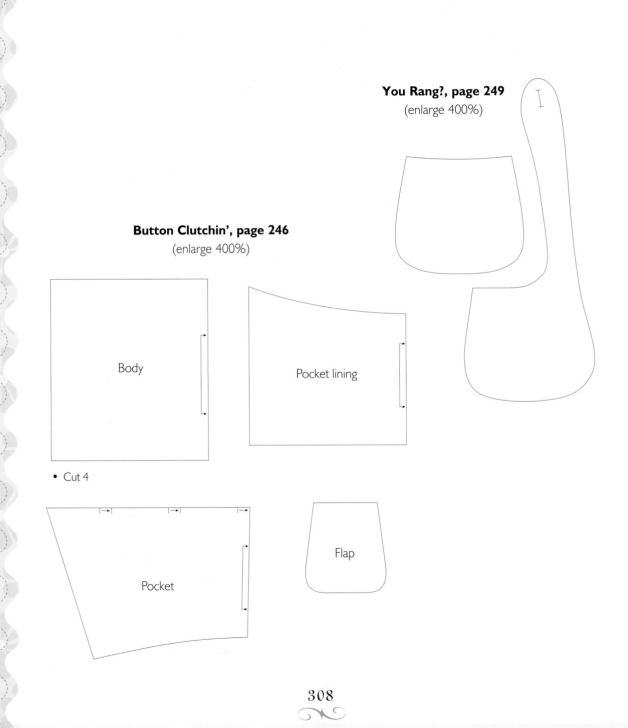

You Rang?, page 249

(enlarge 400%)

Button Clutchin', page 246

(enlarge 400%)

Body

Pocket lining

• Cut 4

Pocket

Flap

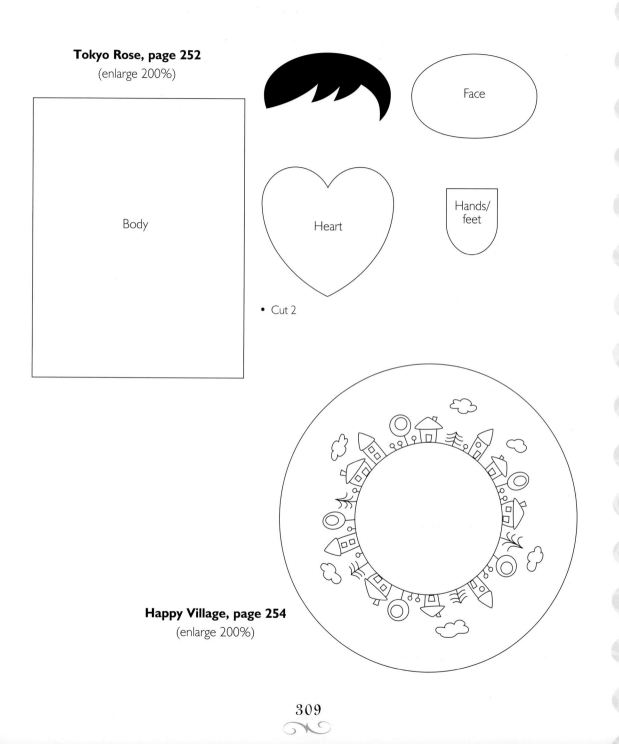

Tokyo Rose, page 252
(enlarge 200%)

Body

Face

Heart

Hands/feet

• Cut 2

Happy Village, page 254
(enlarge 200%)

309

Snap Attack, page 268

(enlarge 400%)

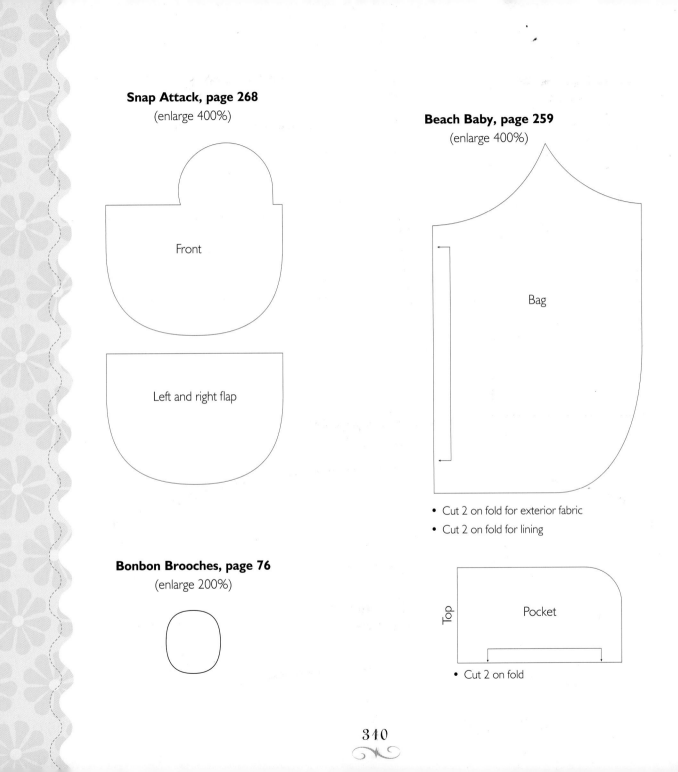

Front

Left and right flap

Beach Baby, page 259

(enlarge 400%)

Bag

- Cut 2 on fold for exterior fabric
- Cut 2 on fold for lining

Bonbon Brooches, page 76

(enlarge 200%)

Top

Pocket

- Cut 2 on fold

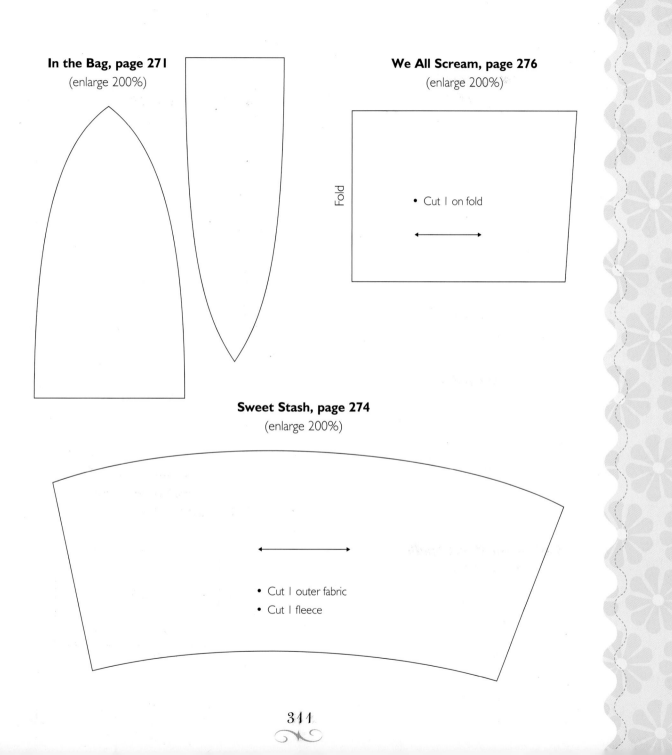

In the Bag, page 271

(enlarge 200%)

We All Scream, page 276

(enlarge 200%)

Fold

• Cut 1 on fold

Sweet Stash, page 274

(enlarge 200%)

• Cut 1 outer fabric
• Cut 1 fleece

index

Accessories
Belt It Out, 208
Bonbon Brooch, 76
Card Cache, 222
Flowing Scarf, 52
Making the Band, 168
Obi Belt, 44
Sweet Stash, 274
Too Cool Cuff, 20

Bags
Beach Baby, 259
Bling Sling, 226
Button Clutchin', 246
Clutch Me Tightly, 238
Crafty Carrier, 233
Diaper Snug, 256
Dream On, 281
Eco Chic, 236
Handy Hook Holder, 278
Happy Village, 254
In the Bag, 271
Just in Case, 224
Passport, Please, 112
Picnic Partner, 165
Rapper Wrapper, 265
Snap Attack, 268
Tokyo Rose, 252
Wooly Tote, 230
Yo, Chica, 262
Yoga to Go, 241
You Rang, 249

Home Décor
A Bird for All Seasons, 110
All Buttoned Up, 178
Birdie Mobile, 40
Book Nook, 27
Hold Anything, 108
Home Sweet Home Coasters, 142
I ❤ You Coasters, 122
Patchwork Doorstop, 116
Pocket Placemats, 170
Sew Pretty Ornaments, 98
Soft Spheres, 36
Zippin' Along, 244

Keepsakes
Hearts on a String, 130
Keep Your Place, 124
Under Cover, 284
Undercover Portfolio, 132
We All Scream, 276
Wedding Memories, 119

Pillows
Airborne Appliqué, 73
Child's Play, 91
Eco On-the-Go, 198
I Do, 138
In Bloom, 30
New Neutral, 196
Quick Change, 66
Refab Modern, 47
Ribbon Rounds, 182
Sitting Pretty Cushion, 6
Spot On, 218
Sweet Dreams, 9
Sweet Tooth, 127
Trapunto Trio, 215

Pincushions
At Your Fingertips, 100
Bee Sewing, 162
Close-Knit Friends, 204
Corsage Pins, 201
Dress It Up, 154
No-Sew Kitsch, 148
Pin Pals, 210
Pinning Zoo, 176
Sew Convenient, 95
Sew on the Go, 150
Timeless Treasures, 102
Whipstitch It Good, 213

Potholders
Dot's Diner, 194
Girly Garden, 173
Log In, 188
Nifty Fifties, 144
Now and Zen, 152
Recipe for Happiness, 105
Retro Active, 157
Salsa Softies, 180
Scorchin', 185
Spiffy Potholders, 88
Sweet Treat, 206
That's Amore, 70
Yo-Yo Go, 160

Quilts
Autumn Breeze, 24
Blue Pools, 59
Bright Teeth, 82
Center of Attention, 57
Hearts on Fire, 14
Hop in Your Step, 38
One Tree Hill, 12
Spinning in Orbit, 85
Square Deal, 54
The Elusive Batiki Bird, 62
Yard Tale, 32

Stuffed Toys
Cuddle Drops, 79
Cute + Curious, 191
Feeling Needled, 19
Wake, Rattle, and Stroll, 136